PRAISE FOR *NURSE ON BOARD.* *TO THE BOARDROOM*

"Connie Curran has truly been a gifted leader and scholar throughout my nursing career. This, her last book, continues her legacy as a transformational leader. The challenge she offers us all as nurse leaders is to sharpen our skills to be influential, strategic leaders on governance boards and, ultimately, to chair boards. The pages of this book are filled with wisdom and practical approaches, from assessment of individual skills to assessment of board skills. Some of our nation's finest nurse leaders interject their advice in the many true-life stories throughout the book. This is truly a must-read for everyone interested in governance, board membership, and influencing healthcare reformation."

–Linda C. Lewis, MSA, BSN, RN, NEA-BC, FACHE, FAAN
Chief ANCC Officer
American Nurses Credentialing Center

"Nurse on Board provides an excellent overview of board basics and trends and is essential reading not only for nurses aspiring to board appointments, but for those already on boards. This book clearly articulates the fundamentals for all who consider or seek a board appointment but aren't sure what that commitment involves."

–Angela Barron McBride, PhD, RN, FAAN
Distinguished Professor and University Dean Emerita, Indiana University School of Nursing
Board Member, Indiana University Health

"This is an excellent primer for nurses seeking to broaden their influence by serving as a healthcare board member."

–Linda Burnes Bolton, DrPH, RN, FAAN
Vice President, Nursing Cedars-Sinai Medical Center
President, American Organization of Nurse Executives 2015

"Connie Curran left us a true gift in her most recent book, Nurse on Board: Planning Your Path to the Boardroom. *Whether you are aspiring to your first position on a board or have served on many boards, you will find Curran's work an invaluable guidebook. Not only will you learn the basics—such as roles and responsibilities of board members, types of boards, or the ABC's of board membership—but you will also explore the more advanced concepts of independence, transparency, compensation, and evaluation of board member service. Curran also focuses on understanding financial management and hospital board service. I highly recommend her seminal work."*

–Lisa Wright Eichelberger, PhD, RN
Dean, College of Health
Clayton State University

NURSE
ON BOARD

planning your path to the boardroom

CONNIE CURRAN, EdD, RN, FAAN

Sigma Theta Tau International
Honor Society of Nursing®

The Honor Society of Nursing, Sigma Theta Tau International (STTI) is a nonprofit organization founded in 1922 whose mission is to support the learning, knowledge, and professional development of nurses committed to making a difference in health worldwide. Members include practicing nurses, instructors, researchers, policymakers, entrepreneurs, and others. STTI's nearly 500 chapters are located at 695 institutions of higher education throughout Armenia, Australia, Botswana, Brazil, Canada, Colombia, England, Ghana, Hong Kong, Japan, Kenya, Lebanon, Malawi, Mexico, the Netherlands, Pakistan, Portugal, Singapore, South Africa, South Korea, Swaziland, Sweden, Taiwan, Tanzania, Thailand, the United Kingdom, and the United States of America. More information about STTI can be found online at www.nursingsociety.org.

Sigma Theta Tau International
550 West North Street
Indianapolis, IN, USA 46202

To order additional books, buy in bulk, or order for corporate use, contact Nursing Knowledge International at 888.NKI.4YOU (888.654.4968/US and Canada) or +1.317.634.8171 (outside US and Canada).

To request a review copy for course adoption, email solutions@nursingknowledge.org or call 888. NKI.4YOU (888.654.4968/US and Canada) or +1.317.634.8171 (outside US and Canada).

To request author information, or for speaker or other media requests, contact Marketing, Honor Society of Nursing, Sigma Theta Tau International at 888.634.7575 (US and Canada) or +1.317.634.8171 (outside US and Canada).

ISBN: 9781938835926
EPUB ISBN: 9781938835933
PDF ISBN: 9781938835940
MOBI ISBN: 9781938835957

Library of Congress Cataloging-in-Publication data

Curran, Connie L., author.
  Nurse on board : planning your path to the boardroom / Connie Curran.
    p. ; cm.
  Includes bibliographical references.
  ISBN 978-1-938835-92-6 (print : alk. paper)—ISBN 978-1-938835-93-3 (epub)—
ISBN 978-1-938835-94-0 (pdf)—ISBN 978-1-938835-95-7 (mobi)
  I. Sigma Theta Tau International, issuing body. II. Title.
  [DNLM: 1. Nurse Administrators—United States. 2. Career Mobility—United States. 3. Governing Board—United States. 4. Leadership—United States. 5. Nurse's Role—United States. WY 105]
  RT89.3
  362.17'3068--dc23
                          2015025652

First Printing, 2015

Publisher: Dustin Sullivan
Acquisitions Editor: Emily Hatch
Editorial Coordinator: Paula Jeffers
Cover Designer: Rebecca Batchelor
Interior Design/Layout: Rebecca Batchelor

Principal Book Editor: Carla Hall
Development and Project Editor: Tonya Maddox Cupp
Copy Editor: Teresa Artman
Proofreader: Gill Editorial Services
Indexer: Larry Sweazy

DEDICATION

This book is dedicated to all the nurses who have marched into the boardroom and to all those preparing to be board ready.

"For we who nurse, our nursing is something which, unless we are making progress every year, every month, every week, we are going back. No system shall endure which does not march."
–Florence Nightingale

PUBLISHER'S NOTE

The Honor Society of Nursing, Sigma Theta Tau International would like to express its deep respect and admiration for the life and work of Connie Curran. Her passionate commitment toward empowering nurses to pursue and achieve positions of leadership will have a lasting impact on the profession and those who heeded her call to action. Her legacy of leadership resides in the words she left, the programs she built, and the actions of the people she inspired along the way.

–From Connie's many friends and colleagues
from Sigma Theta Tau International

ACKNOWLEDGMENTS

So many individuals and organizations have contributed to my governance expertise. Like most nurses, I had no knowledge of boards or their roles in, responsibilities to, or power of creating great organizations. My first board was the American Nurses Association Education Council. That council was basically an advisory board providing advice to the ANA board on education issues and policies. There were 10 fabulous nurses serving as members of that advisory council. They were well prepared for meetings, engaged in robust discussions, able to disagree without being disagreeable, and they accomplished significant work at the meetings. That first governance experience was enlightening and inspirational. I realized that my personal mission of improving the quantity and quality of patients' lives could be actualized through work on boards.

Work on a college board and the board of a rehabilitation institution were my next governance assignments. These boards were very different from each other. The college board was large, congenial, and informal; and the rehabilitation board was small, intense, and formal. These experiences helped me learn that although board processes may be very different, there is no single right way to govern.

I went on to serve on dozens of nonprofit and corporate boards in the past 20 years. I am especially grateful to Luke McGuinness, who taught me about great governance. He was the CEO of MacNeal Hospital in Berwyn, Illinois. Luke is a master at creating a team of his board and his managers. His sense of urgency and demands for excellence were contagious. He led the development of great healthcare organizations that improved the lives of patients, caregivers, and the community. It was a privilege to work with Luke.

I spent 10 years on the board of Silver Cross Hospital in Joliet, Illinois, working with their CEO Paul Pawlak. I served as chairman of the Silver

Cross board and witnessed the power of the organization's belief that if you can measure it, you can move it. It was thrilling to partner with Paul, his management team, and the Silver Cross board to create world-class care for the people of Joliet. It was great to be part of the team when Silver Cross was acknowledged as a Solucient Top 100 Hospital for 7 consecutive years.

I spent the last 10 years on the board of Hospira, Inc. Hospira was a new company spun from Abbott Laboratories. The founding CEO was Christopher Begley, and David Jones was the first chairman of the board. They were brilliant in their work of creating a board out of a group of strangers. I am grateful for the leadership lessons I learned through my work with these two wonderful men. Organizations endure and create many changes in a 10-year period. Hospira has continued to grow, improve, and create great healthcare products. Today we have the dynamic, warm, and motivational CEO, Mike Ball. He is a fabulous communicator who has been able to gain the admiration and dedication of employees worldwide. Being a member of the Hospira board has added significantly to my knowledge of best governance practices.

I will always be grateful to DePaul University, where I earned my master's degree in nursing many years ago. I was a recipient of their commitment to helping students discover their gifts, develop those gifts, and then use those gifts to create a better world. I have served on the DePaul University board of directors for several years. Father Dennis Holtschneider, DePaul's president, is a warm, charismatic, and tireless leader. Every time I am with Dennis, I become grateful for all of my blessings and am inspired to do more and do better. DePaul is masterful at trustee engagement and shared several of its tools in this book.

At the time of writing this book, I served as chair of the board of the DrVry Education Group. The purpose of the DeVry Education Group is to empower its students to achieve their educational and career goals. DeVry is a global provider of educational services and the parent organization of American University of the Caribbean School of Medicine, Becker Professional Education, Carrington College, Chamberlain College of Nursing, DeVry Brasil, DeVry University, Ross University School of Medicine, and Ross University School of Veterinary. These institutions offer a wide array of programs in business, healthcare, technology, accounting, and finance. I was a member of the DeVry board for 8 years and their board chairman for a year. While at DeVry, I also served on the boards of Ross and Chamberlain.

I am grateful to the members of the DeVry board of trustees for electing me to chair the board. Only 3% of all corporate board chairs in the U.S. are women (Catalyst, 2013), and this exceptional board had the courage and confidence to appoint a woman (and a nurse) as its chairperson! Daniel Hamburger is president and CEO of the DeVry Education Group. I am grateful for the opportunity to partner with Daniel, an intelligent, hardworking executive who believes in *doing well by doing good*.

I am appreciative of the nurses and search executives who have shared their governance experience and wisdom throughout this book. Their interviews are provocative, insightful, and practical—and feel like advice from a friend.

Finally, I am grateful to Sigma Theta Tau International (STTI) for its dedication to nurses around the world. This book is evidence of the STTI commitment to developing and supporting nurse leaders.

For more than 20 years, Beth Ingram supported and encouraged my governance work. I am very grateful. Lin Grensing-Pophal's patience, enthusiasm, and hard work were a source of joy throughout the preparation of this book.

ABOUT THE AUTHOR

Connie Curran, EdD, RN, FAAN, was founder and chief executive officer of Best on Board, a national organization focused on educating and certifying healthcare trustees. She was the founding executive director of C-Change, a national organization focused on the eradication of cancer. C-Change participants, roughly 150 in all, included the heads of federal and state governmental agencies, for-profit corporations, the motion picture industry, and nonprofit groups whose missions related to cancer. Former President George H. W. Bush and First Lady Barbara Bush served as co-chairs, with Senator Dianne Feinstein as vice chair.

Curran was the founder, president, and chief executive officer of CurranCare, LLC from 1995 to 2000. CurranCare was a national management and consulting services organization that delivered dynamic leadership to the healthcare industry. Cardinal Health acquired CurranCare, and Curran served as president of Cardinal Health Consulting Services, providing leadership to approximately 200 consultants. She held a variety of executive positions in academic and healthcare organizations. She was the chief nursing officer of Montefiore Medical Center in the Bronx, vice president of the American Hospital Association, and dean at the Medical College of Wisconsin.

A prolific scholar in the field, Curran has more than 200 publications and several research programs to her credit. She served as the director of two of the most comprehensive national studies on staff recruitment, retention, and labor market participation. More recently, she had co-authored books on hospital–physician integration, hospital redesign, and optimized home care integration. She served as the editor of *Nursing Economic$* for 18 years. Her most recent book, *Claiming the Corner Office: Executive Leadership Lessons for Nurses*, was published in 2013.

She graduated from the Harvard Business School program for company owners and presidents and served on numerous corporate, privately held, and nonprofit boards, including serving as chair of the board of directors of Silver Cross Hospital. Until her untimely death in 2014, she served as chair of the board of DeVry, Inc., and served as director for the boards for Hospira, Inc., DePaul University, Chicago Lurie Children's Hospital, and the University of Wisconsin Foundation.

ABOUT THE CONTRIBUTORS

LAURIE BENSON

Laurie Benson, BSN, RN, is an accomplished corporate executive, entrepreneur, and corporate board director. During the past 25 years, she has served on seven corporate boards in the technology, finance, insurance, manufacturing, and services industries, and currently serves on five corporate boards. Additionally, she has expertise and is actively engaged in the healthcare industry through board service, executive leadership, and innovation roles. Benson serves as a C-suite advisor to CEOs, presidents, and entrepreneurs on complex issues including board governance, strategy, business growth, innovation, high-performance teams, human resources, and succession planning. She developed this capability through her 25 years as CEO and cofounder of Inacom Information Systems (1984–2009), where she grew this IT systems integrator to $80M at time of sale to Core BTS. The company consistently achieved high-level national industry partner rankings with Cisco, Microsoft, Hewlett-Packard, IBM, and EMC, including being recognized as Microsoft's Worldwide Partner of the Year for client-centered implementations. Benson has received numerous awards, most recently the UW Madison Distinguished Alumni Award 2013; UW Madison Chancellor's Entrepreneurial Achievement Award 2013; *In Business* 2011 Executive Hall of Fame; ATHENA Award 2010; and National SBA Women in Business Champion 2009. In addition, she was recognized in *Directors & Boards* magazine's "Directors to Watch" 2013. Benson's ongoing leadership and involvement in healthcare organizations originally stemmed from her University of Wisconsin–Madison bachelor of science degree in nursing and continues today through her ongoing leadership on the school of nursing advisory board.

She demonstrates leadership in board governance as an active member of the National Association of Corporate Directors (NACD), Women Corporate Directors (WCD), Women Business Leaders in Healthcare (WBL), and Global Board Ready Women. She is an accomplished speaker on leadership, culture, innovation, including leading change in healthcare.

GLADYS CAMPBELL

Gladys Campbell, MSN, RN, FAAN, is an independent healthcare consultant and leadership coach in the Pacific Northwest. Prior to that, she was CEO of the Northwest Organization of Nurse Executives (NWONE) and CNE and senior leader for clinical strategy for the Washington State Hospital Association. She began her career in Seattle where she graduated from the University of Washington School of Nursing. After graduation, she was commissioned as an officer in the United States Public Health Service and worked in successive leadership positions in Boston, New York, and Washington, DC, where she completed her graduate degree at the Catholic University of America. While in Washington, DC, she spent 20 years at the National Institutes of Health Clinical Center, where she became an associate chief nurse executive (CNE) for the organization and co-led the development of a unit-based model of clinical research. After retiring from the United States Public Health Service, Campbell worked in Nashville, Tennessee, as an associate CNE and as executive director for the Tennessee Regional Research Institute of Saint Thomas Medical Center. In November of 2003, Campbell relocated to Portland, Oregon, where she was the assistant administrator for Nursing and Patient Care Services at the Providence Saint Vincent Medical Center. In January 2007, Campbell became the CEO for NWONE and the CNE and senior leader for clinical strategy for the Washington State Hospital Association. She served in this role for nine years before leaving to become an independent consultant. Campbell has served as a fellow in the American Nurses Credentialing Center's Magnet Appraiser Program and a fellow in the College of Critical Care Medicine; she is a past president of the American Association of Critical-Care Nurses. She is a career long member of the American Nurses Association and Sigma Theta Tau International, a member of the American Organization of Nurse Executives, a past member of the board of directors for the Certification Corporation of AACN, and a fellow in the American Academy of Nursing. She has been a member of the editorial board of Clinical Issues in Critical Care Nursing and is a published author and a frequent speaker with an extensive list of presentations to her credit.

JOANNE DISCH

Joanne Disch, PhD, RN, FAAN, is professor ad honorem at the University of Minnesota School of Nursing. Previously, she was the director of the Katharine J. Densford International Center for Nursing Leadership and the Katherine R. and C. Walton Lillehei Chair in Nursing Leadership at the School. She received her BSN from the University of Wisconsin–Madison; her MSN in cardiovascular nursing from the University of Alabama in Birmingham; and her PhD in nursing from the University of Michigan. Starting her career as a staff nurse in cardiovascular intensive care, Disch had her first board experience with the American Association of Critical-Care Nurses, having been encouraged to become active by a mentor from graduate school. Over the course of her career, she eventually served as a chief nurse executive in two major medical centers; she served as interim dean at the University of Minnesota School of Nursing, USA; and she held numerous national leadership positions, such as president of the American Association of Critical-Care Nurses, chair of the American Nurses Association Committee on Nursing Practice Standards and Guidelines, chair of the University Hospital Consortium's Chief Nurse

Executive Council, and board member and chair of the national board of AARP. Disch has served as a board member on several major healthcare boards, such as Allina Health and the National Center for Healthcare Leadership. Currently she is a member of the board of Aurora Health Care and chair of the board of Chamberlain College of Nursing. She is the immediate past president of the American Academy of Nursing. Her research has centered on nurse/physician relationships and quality and safety within healthcare organizations. For the past 10 years, she has been a faculty leader for the Quality and Safety Education for Nurses (QSEN) initiative. Disch has lectured and published widely on patient safety and is a coauthor of an *American Journal of Nursing* 2014 Book of the Year Award winning book, *Person and Family Centered Care*. She has received a number of awards for her work, among them the 2015 Marguerite Rodgers Kinney Award for a Distinguished Career from the American Association of Critical-Care Nurses; the Dorothy Garrigus Adams Award for Excellence in Fostering Professional Standards and the Mary Tolle Wright Award for Excellence in Leadership from Sigma Theta Tau International; the President's Award from the American Academy of Nursing; Distinguished Alumna Awards from the Schools of Nursing at the University of Alabama in Birmingham and the University of Wisconsin; and the Distinguished Alumna Award from the University of Wisconsin.

THERESE FITZPATRICK

Therese Fitzpatrick, PhD, RN, is a principal leading the clinical strategy within consulting engagements for the Healthcare Transformation Services business of Philips Healthcare. She has expertise in healthcare strategy, operational productivity, optimization modeling, analytics, clinical staffing, business development, and demand planning. Prior to joining Philips in 2014, Fitzpatrick was a founding partner for two consulting and analytics firms focused on mathematical optimization modeling and logistics science in strategic clinical workforce planning. She served as CEO of a private equity–owned nurse staffing company. After growing revenues to $8+ million annually, she facilitated a merger with another staffing firm to form the largest regional clinical staffing organization in Chicago, doubling revenues in the first year. She built a consulting division that provided hospitals with strategies related to demand planning, staff optimization, and budgeting. Fitzpatrick has served as CNO and COO in both academic and community healthcare systems, including a Top 100 hospital system. Having received certification in negotiating strategy from Harvard University, her leadership practice has focused significantly on improving operations and staff productivity in unionized organizations. She is widely published on nursing optimization, clinical staffing, and clinical activity analysis. Her work on optimization modeling was awarded the Greatest Potential Contribution to Nursing Practice by the Royal College of Surgeons, Ireland. Her research and analysis on the recently implemented staffing legislation in Illinois is becoming a national example of a viable alternative to mandated staffing ratios. In 2013, she coauthored (with Connie Curran) *Claiming the Corner Office: Executive Leadership Lessons for Nurses,* a book that teaches nurses how to develop personal leadership potential in preparation for senior executive positions. Fitzpatrick serves on several boards of directors, including the editorial board of the journal *Nursing Economic$*; Advocate Good Samaritan Hospital, Illinois; Turning Point Community Mental Health Center, Illinois; and the advisory board for the College of Science and Health at DePaul University, Chicago. She is an assistant clinical professor at the University of Illinois–Chicago College of Nursing, Department of Health System Sciences, where she teaches graduate administrative studies. Fitzpatrick received her BSN and MS in nursing administration from DePaul University. She received a PhD in urban studies from the University of Wisconsin–Milwaukee.

JAMES W. GAUSS

James W. Gauss, MHA, is chair of Board Services at Witt/Kieffer, an executive search firm based in Irvine, California, and devoted to health-care, life sciences, higher education, and nonprofit industries. He has more than three decades of experience advising board members and CEOs on board succession planning, skill-set evaluation, and recruiting in periods of rapid change and transformation. He combines industry expertise and research in his work with healthcare, academic, nonprofit, and corporate boards across the country. In his previous role as president and CEO of Witt/Kieffer, Gauss counseled hundreds of boards and search committees on organizational structure, core competencies for successful trustees and C-suite executives, leadership assessment, diversity, and effective onboarding, among many other areas. Currently serving on the National Board of Advisors for the American Hospital Association Center for Healthcare Governance, Gauss thoroughly understands the culture of today's successful boards as well as the needs of high-performing boards in the future. He has recruited business leaders from a broad range of disciplines, is a member of the National Association of Corporate Directors, and has been widely quoted on board issues in general business and in healthcare press, including *Directors & Boards*, *Forbes*, *The Wall Street Journal*, *USA Today*, *CEO Update*, *Trustee*, *Hospitals & Health Networks*, *The Chronicle of Philanthropy*, *Diversity Executive*, *The Chronicle of Higher Education*, *Becker's Hospital Review*, and *Inside Higher Education*. Named by *Bloomberg Businessweek* as one of the top 100 most influential executive search consultants worldwide, he has deep relationships with boards and industry leaders within healthcare, insurance/managed care, and higher education, as well as with a wide variety of other businesses and foundations. Gauss assists boards in assessing where gaps exist in current areas of expertise, planning for future board member succession, and recruiting trustees and directors who have the vision and skills to achieve an organization's strategic goals.

He is widely recognized for his work on diversity and disparities of care issues. In addition to being widely published in this area, he recently served two terms as a board member with the American Hospital Association Institute for Diversity and chaired a task force on Advancing Diversity in Governance and Leadership. Gauss holds an MHA from Washington University in St. Louis, Missouri, and a BA from Lakeland College in Sheboygan, Wisconsin. He regularly presents to healthcare and business audiences nationally.

SUSAN GROENWALD

Susan Groenwald, PhD, RN, ANEF, FAAN, is a pioneer who helped develop the specialty of oncology nursing. While holding a joint appointment at Rush University and Rush Medical Center, she was elected to the inaugural board of the Oncology Nursing Society (ONS); co-led a team that created the first standards for oncology nursing practice; and helped found the first chapter of the ONS in Chicago, for which she served as vice president. Groenwald was director of the Oncology Nursing Graduate Program at Rush University and authored a comprehensive oncology nursing textbook, which received an *American Journal of Nursing* Book Award in 1988 and again in 1997. Additionally, she coauthored a cancer symptom management textbook and was on the editorial boards of three cancer nursing journals. She created and managed one of the first telephonic cancer symptom management programs to serve cancer patients throughout the United States. Groenwald spent 20 years in the business sector growing and developing companies that were later sold. In 2006, she became president of Chamberlain College of Nursing, growing Chamberlain to one of the largest nursing colleges in the country. Under her leadership, the college has graduated more than 18,000 BSN nurses and established a master's degree program with five specialty tracks including informatics, education, administration, healthcare policy, and family nurse practitioner. She also established a DNP-degree program with two tracks. Groenwald spearheaded the development of partnerships with key nursing organizations, which led to the establishment of the National League of Nursing/Chamberlain Center for the Advancement of Nursing Education and the Sigma Theta Tau International and Chamberlain College of Nursing Center for Excellence in Nursing Education. She received her BSN and MSN from Rush University; a certificate in business administration from the University of Illinois at Chicago; and a Doctor of Philosophy (PhD), Higher Education/Higher Education Administration from Capella University.

SUSAN HASSMILLER

Susan Hassmiller, PhD, RN, FAAN, who joined the Robert Wood Johnson Foundation (RWJF) in 1997, is presently the Robert Wood Johnson Foundation senior adviser for nursing. In this role, she shapes and leads the Foundation's nursing strategies in an effort to create a higher quality of care in the United States for people, families, and communities. Drawn to the Foundation's "organizational advocacy for the less fortunate and underserved," Hassmiller is helping to assure that RWJF's commitments in nursing have a broad and lasting national impact. In partnership with AARP, she directs the Foundation's Future of Nursing: Campaign for Action, which seeks to ensure that everyone in America can live a healthier life, supported by a system in which nurses are essential partners in providing care and promoting health. This 50-state and District of Columbia effort strives to implement the recommendations of the Institute of Medicine's report on the Future of Nursing: Leading Change, Advancing Health. Hassmiller served as the report's study director. She is also serving as co-director of the Future of Nursing Scholars program, an initiative that provides scholarships, mentoring and leadership development activities, and postdoctoral research funding to build the leadership capacity of nurse educators and researchers. Previously, she served with the Health Resources and Services Administration, where she was the executive director of the U.S. Public Health Service Primary Care Policy Fellowship and worked on other national and international primary care initiatives. She also has worked in public health settings at the local and state level and taught public health nursing at the University of Nebraska and George Mason University in Virginia. Hassmiller, who has been very involved with the Red Cross in many capacities, was a member of the National Board of Governors for the American Red Cross, serving as chair of the Disaster and Chapter Services Committee and national chair of the 9/11 Recovery Program. She is currently a member of the National Nursing Committee, and is serving as immediate past board chair for the Central New Jersey Red Cross. She has been involved in Red Cross disaster relief efforts in the United States and abroad, including tornadoes in the Midwest, Hurricane Andrew, September 11th, the 2004 Florida hurricanes, Hurricane Katrina, and the tsunami in Indonesia. Hassmiller is a member of the Institute of Medicine, a fellow in the American Academy of Nursing, a member of the Joint Commission's National Nurse Advisory Council, Meridian Health System Board of Directors, the Health Resources and Services Administration National Advisory Committee for Nurse Education and Practice, and the CMS National Nurse Steering Committee. She is a founding member of the National Nurses on Boards Coalition. Hassmiller received a PhD in nursing administration and health policy from George Mason University in Fairfax, Virginia, master's degrees in health education from Florida State University and community health nursing from the University of Nebraska Medical Center, and a bachelor's degree in nursing from Florida State University. She is the recipient of numerous national awards in addition to receiving the distinguished alumna award for all the schools of nursing from which she graduated and two honorary doctoral degrees. Most notably, Hassmiller is the 2009 recipient of the

Florence Nightingale Medal, the highest international honor given to a nurse by the International Committee of the Red Cross.

DANIEL J. PESUT

Daniel J. Pesut, PhD, RN, PMHCNS-BC, FAAN, is a professor of nursing in the Nursing Population Health and Systems Cooperative Unit of the School of Nursing at the University of Minne-sota and director of the Katharine J. Densford International Center for Nursing Leadership. He holds the Katherine R. and C. Walton Lillehei Chair in Nursing Leadership. Pesut is a popular author, speaker, coach, and consultant and is known for his ability to inspire and help people access and develop creative ideas and design innovative solutions to challenging problems. He is internationally known for his work in nursing education, creative teaching–learning methods, self-regulation of health status, clinical reasoning, futures thinking, executive coaching, and leadership development in the health professions. He is a certified Hudson Institute of Santa Barbara coach. He is past president (2003–2005) of the Honor Society of Nursing, Sigma Theta Tau International. He served on the board of trustees of the Plexus Institute, which is an organization with the mission to foster the health of individuals, families, and communities, organizations, and our natural environment by helping people use concepts emerging from the new science of complexity. He is a fellow in the American Academy of Nursing and a board certified clinical nurse specialist in adult psychiatric mental health nursing. Pesut is the recipient of many awards, including an Army Commendation Award while on active duty (1975–1978) in the U.S. Army Nurse Corps; the Honor Society of Nursing, Sigma Theta Tau International Edith Moore Copeland Founder's Award for Creativity; The American Assembly for Men In Nursing Luther Christman Award; Distinguished Alumni Awards from Northern Illinois University School of Nursing-College of Health and Human

Services; as well as a number of other distinguished alumni, teaching, mentoring, and leadership awards. Pesut earned a PhD in nursing from the University of Michigan, a master's degree in psychiatric mental health nursing from the University of Texas Health Science Center in San Antonio, Texas, and a bachelor of science degree in nursing from Northern Illinois University, DeKalb, Illinois. He has completed certificates in management development from Harvard Institute for Higher Education, core mediation skills training from the International Association of Dispute Resolution (IARD), and integral studies from Fielding Graduate University.

LINDA PROCCI

Linda Procci, PhD, RN, is a clinical professor of nursing at the University of Wisconsin–Madison. Procci recently retired after 17 years as vice president of service line operations at Cedars-Sinai Medical Center in Los Angeles. Prior to that, she served for 15 years as vice president and COO at Good Samaritan Hospital in Los Angeles. She also previously held the position of director of training in nursing, University Affiliated Program, Children's Hospital of Los Angeles. Her extensive leadership and management experience in complex, academic, tertiary, and integrated healthcare organizations have led to measurable success/satisfaction for stakeholders, improved clinical outcomes, and positive financial returns. She currently serves on the University of Wisconsin-Madison (UW) Foundation Board, the Board of Visitors for the UW School of Nursing, and the Wise & Healthy Aging Board. Procci holds BS and MS degrees in nursing from UW Madison and a PhD in education from the University of Southern California.

TABLE OF CONTENTS

FOREWORD

Introducing a trailblazing icon—a visionary innovator and fellow board member who was also a brilliant driver of change and a consummate politician—is not an easy task. But Connie Curran, this book's author, navigated the world of nursing, healthcare, and executive management effortlessly: At least it appeared that way to me.

Connie worked tirelessly to advance her beloved nursing profession, pulling the healthcare industry along with her. Her mission was clear, her voice was strong, and her many talents were laser focused on a single passion: getting more nurses on boards. Connie singlehandedly led nurses from the bedside to the governing table—by example, via her books, and through hands-on mentoring.

I recall one morning sitting at the breakfast table watching *CBS Sunday Morning,* and there was my friend Connie on the television talking about changes in life, walking the streets of San Francisco after her years in Chicago. She was more than open to change; she invited it in because she saw its potential to advance the self.

She believed in her heart of hearts that the profession needs all the gifts its members possess if we are to transform healthcare into all that it can be. Leading change, you see, was her gift.

I first met Connie in the 1980s, when I was a corporate nurse at the pioneering for-profit healthcare company HCA (Hospital Corporation of America). Connie, representing the American Hospital Association (AHA), served as executive director at the ASNSA, a precursor to AONE. I can remember the call as if it happened yesterday. Her amazing voice came through clearly on my landline to inform me that she was coming to visit me in Nashville because HCA was the largest member of AHA. Although I had no clue who she was or why she was coming, one thing was clear: She was on her way. She was determined to show our corporate leaders the value that only an engaged nursing professional could add. One by one, HCA executives—from Dr. Thomas Frist, Sr., one of HCA's founders and the "father of the modern for-profit hospital system," to David Williamson, then a board member of AHA—became aware of the invaluable perspective and untapped leadership that nursing could bring to bear on healthcare's transformation.

A few years later, when the Kellogg Foundation awarded a grant titled "National Commission on Nursing Implementation Project," chairman Vivian DeBack, PhD, RN, FAAN, and I were searching for a powerful keynote speaker who could drive the introduction of change in nursing education, practice, and service. Only one name came to mind: Connie Curran.

My esteemed colleague omitted from *Nurse on Board* one critical fact: Decision-making at the board level is painful. She knew that truth all too well. Being on a board requires deep reflective thought that your colleagues might not see as positive and, yet, the organization's very survival depends on the board's willingness to make tough decisions.

Connie realized that no nurse is on a board to be a nurse. Rather, this responsibility centers on being able to show, against the backdrop of patient care, the knowledge the organization needs to have to be successful. I know for a fact that Connie made very difficult decisions at the board level—decisions that, while heartfelt, caused her difficulty because of their impact on the profession she loved so much. Often, these decisions came during times when an organization's very survival was in question. Through layoffs and union strikes, Connie continued to fight feverishly to keep organizations alive through valiant decision-making.

One of my colleagues told me about Connie visiting her organization to find ways to resolve organizational issues through some tough negotiations with the hospital board's leadership. Connie worked with the management team to strengthen institutional knowledge and create new standards of success. Today, that organization not only survives, it flourishes. Connie helped the board navigate through a tough set of obstacles to see the opportunities on the horizon.

As a corporate nurse, I clearly see her impact on nursing and our healthcare system. I have gained new insights from reading Connie's editorial work, especially her groundbreaking book, *Claiming the Corner Office.* Not only did this book encourage nurses to make their way into management and the executive suite, but it also gave them a practical road map for getting there.

In academe, she jettisoned conventional wisdom to push for better education for nurses, clearer career paths into management and beyond, and board seats for nurses ready to govern. Until Connie came on the scene, there were few, if any, nurses in the boardroom. Connie realized that patients need advocates, and nurses are spectacularly willing and able to provide that advocacy. More importantly, what had been learned at the bedside needed to be made clear to those in the boardroom. Connie championed what no one at the time recognized: that nurses on boards are a *must* for leadership in healthcare.

Connie achieved these groundbreaking accomplishments while maintaining deep relationships with her family and her friends. I know she especially cherished her daughter, Melissa, and grandson, Oliver, because she told me so. She drew her strength from a rich network of lifelong supporters who recognized her for all she was—an activist for change, a supremely talented collaborator and motivator, and, most important of all, a woman who cared deeply. I remain extremely proud to be able to call her my friend.

Today, as I work to advance Connie's work posthumously, I reflect on the memorial services at her alma mater, DePaul University. Connie will forever be remembered by many, but her greatest accomplishment, outside that of a personal nature, was her executive leadership in the profession of nursing. She pushed limits and dissolved boundaries in ways that only a handful of pioneers can.

–Roy L. Simpson, DNP, RN, DPNAP, FAAN
Vice President, Nursing, Cerner Corporation

INSTITUTE OF MEDICINE CALLS FOR NURSES TO SERVE ON BOARDS

Donna Shalala, PhD, the Institute of Medicine (IOM) chair for the Committee on the Future of Nursing and secretary for the U.S. Health and Human Services Department under President Bill Clinton, realized the importance of nurses being represented at leadership tables in 2009, after listening to testimony on Capitol Hill on health reform. While several physicians, an attorney, a pharmaceutical representative, and one or two policymakers testified on how to improve patient care in our country, Shalala noted the absence of a nurse. She told me afterward, "I couldn't believe no nurse testified—that needs to change."

Shalala sought to alter the dearth of nurses participating in leadership discussions with the IOM Committee's release of the landmark report *The Future of Nursing: Leading Change, Advancing Health.* The report specifically called for nurses to take on increased leadership roles—including board service—to help improve America's health and health care systems:

By virtue of its numbers and adaptive capacity, the nursing profession has the potential to effect wide-reaching changes in the health care system. Nurses' regular, close proximity to patients and scientific understanding of care processes across the continuum of care give them a unique ability to act as partners with other health professionals and to lead in the improvement and redesign of the health care system and its many practice environments (Institute of Medicine, 2011, p. 3).

In the years since the report's release, the nursing community has galvanized around implementing the IOM report recommendations, including placing more nurses on boards. The need is great: The American Hospital Association (2014) reports that only 5% of hospital board seats are occupied by nurses, despite nurses' expertise on the patient experience, quality and safety, and customer satisfaction in healthcare delivery and performance (Hassmiller & Combes, 2012). In contrast, physicians occupied 20% of board positions (AHA, 2014).

In 2014, 19 leading nursing organizations joined with the Robert Wood Johnson Foundation and AARP to form the Nurses on Boards Coalition. The group seeks to place 10,000 nurses on corporate and nonprofit health-related boards by 2020. The effort is part of a broader movement by the Future of Nursing: Campaign for Action, a nationwide initiative led by the Robert Wood Johnson Foundation and AARP to improve health through nursing. The campaign works at both the national level and in the states, engaging with consumers, nurses, other clinicians, insurers, health care systems, employers, educators, funders, and policymakers—all the stakeholders who need to be involved in system change—to advance the IOM's recommendations.

The Campaign for Action seeks to fulfill Connie Curran's lifelong goal of placing more qualified nurses on boards. It also offers a fertile place for nurses at all levels to further their leadership skills and expertise. To get involved, go to www.campaignforaction.org and click on your state. Join us to promote nursing leadership and help us to place 10,000 nurses on boards by 2020.

–Susan B. Hassmilller, PhD, RN, FAAN

REFERENCES

American Hospital Association. (2014). AHA hospital statistics, 2014 Edition. Chicago, IL: Author.

Committee on the Robert Wood Johnson Foundation Initiative on the Future of Nursing, at the Institute of Medicine. (2011). The future of nursing: Leading change, advancing health. Washington, DC: National Academies Press.

Hassmiller, S., & Combes, J. (2012). Nurse leaders in the boardroom. Journal of Healthcare Management, 57(8).

INTRODUCTION

"The time is always right to do right." –Dr. Martin Luther King, Jr.

"System fails when people with ability don't have authority and people with authority don't have ability." –Amit Kalantri

"Public, private, and governmental health care decision makers at every level should include representation from nursing on boards, on executive management teams, and in other key leadership positions." –The Future of Nursing: Leading Change, Advancing Health (2011)

As nurses go about their day-to-day duties, whether in staff roles or management-level positions, many fail to realize the critical role that the board of directors (BOD) plays in every aspect of their clinical lives, from the types and numbers of patients they serve, to their pay, to the physicians admitted to practice, and even to quality outcome expectations. The fact of the matter is that the BOD has responsibility for all of these things, often without expert input from nurses.

Nurses represent the largest labor force in hospitals, are the largest human resource expense and, most importantly, are closest to the patients, their families, the physicians, and many other key stakeholders. Yet they have little to no input into the governance of healthcare organizations, regardless of their level in those organizations. Only a small fraction of healthcare board positions are held by nurses. The thousands of healthcare organizations, hundreds of disease-focused organizations, and innumerable nursing organizations will be greatly improved when informed nurses serve on their boards.

Although much of this book focuses on healthcare governance, it also explores corporate, advisory, start-up, and corporate boards. There are opportunities for nurses on all of these types of boards. Still, nurses rarely serve them.

This situation demands immediate attention. Over the past few years, organizations—including the Institute of Medicine (IOM), Sigma Theta Tau International (STTI), the American Nurses Association (ANA) Foundation, the American Organization of Nurse Executives (AONE), and the American Academy of Nurses (AAN)—have come forward decrying the woeful lack of nurses on hospital boards and urging nurses to step up to the plate. The problem is multidimensional:

- Nurses do not realize that boards present an opportunity to address their personal and professional passions and missions.

- Nurses are not sure what governance is and how boards work.

- Many nurses do not think they have the skills to serve in governance roles at the board level.

- Boards are often unaware of the skills and abilities that nurses possess.

- Nurses who wish to develop board-ready skills don't know where to begin.

This book addresses these issues via explanation of what boards are and what they do, takes a look at the skills and characteristics required of effective board members (and how to develop these skills), and offers a description of *what* and *who* nurses need to know. You will benefit from interviews with nurses who have held, or currently hold, board-level positions, whether in hospitals, other nonprofit organizations, nursing organizations, or corporate boards. These nurses address their positive and negative board experiences, describe the skills nurses need and may not know they have, and give advice to nurses who want to become "board ready."

I served on more than a dozen corporate boards, a dozen nonprofit boards, and a handful of start-up boards. Throughout this book, I share my experiences and observations about board service. In addition, I have called upon the wisdom of a wide range of other leaders whose personal and practical experiences can help guide your pursuit of effective board service. You will get advice from:

- *Laurie Benson,* BSN, RN, an accomplished corporate executive, entrepreneur, and corporate board director. She has served on seven corporate boards in the technology, finance, insurance, manufacturing, and services industries. Additionally, she has expertise and is actively engaged in the healthcare industry through board service, executive leadership, and innovation roles. As a successful CEO of an IT consulting company, Benson grew revenues from start-up to $80M with 150+ employees across three offices. Currently, she is CEO of a board and strategy consulting company, LSB Unlimited.

- *Gladys Campbell,* MSN, RN, FAAN, is CEO of the Northwest Organization of Nurse Executives and chief nurse executive and senior leader for clinical strategy at the Washington State Hospital Association. Campbell has served as a fellow in the American Nurses Credentialing Center's Magnet Appraiser Program and as a fellow in the College of Critical Care Medicine. She is a past president of the American Association of Critical-Care Nurses, a career-long member of the American Nurses Association and Sigma Theta Tau International, a member of the American Organization of Nurse Executives, a past member of the board of directors for the Certification Corporation of AACN, and a fellow in the American Academy of Nursing.

- *Joanne Disch,* PhD, RN, FAAN, professor ad honorem at the University of Minnesota (UM) School of Nursing. Previously, she was the director of the Katharine J. Densford International

Center for Nursing Leadership and the Katherine R. and C. Walton Lillehei Chair in Nursing Leadership. She has served as a board member on several major healthcare boards, such as Allina Health (in Minnesota) and the National Center for Healthcare Leadership. Currently she is a member of the board of Aurora Health Care and chair of the board of Chamberlain College of Nursing. She is the immediate past president of the American Academy of Nursing.

- *Therese Fitzpatrick,* PhD, RN, is a principal leading the clinical strategy within consulting engagements for the Healthcare Transformation Services business of Philips Healthcare. Fitzpatrick serves on several boards of directors, including the editorial board of the journal *Nursing Economic$*; Advocate Good Samaritan Hospital, Illinois; Turning Point Community Mental Health Center, Illinois; and the advisory board for the College of Science and Health at DePaul University, Chicago.

- *James W. Gauss,* MHA, chair of board services at Witt/Kieffer, an executive search firm in Irvine, California. He has more than three decades of experience advising board members and CEOs on board-succession planning, skill-set evaluation, and recruiting in periods of rapid change and transformation. Currently serving on the National Board of Advisors for the American Hospital Association Center for Healthcare Governance, Gauss thoroughly understands the culture of today's successful boards as well as the needs of high-performing boards in the future.

- *Susan Groenwald,* PhD, RN, ANEF, FAAN, is a pioneer who helped develop the specialty of oncology nursing. While holding a joint appointment at Rush University and Rush Medical Center, she was elected to the inaugural board of the Oncology Nursing Society (ONS), co-led a team that created the first standards for oncology nursing practice, and helped found the first chapter of ONS in Chicago, for which she served as vice president.

- *Susan Hassmiller,* PhD, RN, FAAN. Hassmiller is the Robert Wood Johnson Foundation senior adviser for nursing. She also serves as director of the Future of Nursing: Campaign for Action and codirector of the Future of Nursing Scholars program. Hassmiller has been involved with the Red Cross in many capacities and was a member of the National Board of Governors for the American Red Cross, serving as chair of the Disaster and Chapter Services committee and national chair of the 9/11 Recovery Program. She is now a member of the National Nursing committee and is serving as the board chair for the Central New Jersey Red Cross.

- *Daniel Pesut,* PhD, RN, PMHCNS-BC, FAAN, is professor of nursing in the Nursing Population Health and Systems Cooperative Unit of the School of Nursing at the University of Minnesota and director of the Katharine J. Densford International Center for Nursing Leadership. He is past president (2003–2005) of the Honor Society of Nursing, Sigma Theta Tau International. He served on the board of trustees of the Plexus Institute, which is an organization with the mission to foster the health of individuals, families, communities, organizations, and our natural environment by helping people use concepts emerging from the new science of complexity.

- *Linda Procci,* PhD, RN, is a clinical professor of nursing at the University of Wisconsin–Madison. Procci recently retired after 17 years as vice president of service line operations at Cedars-Sinai Medical Center in Los Angeles. Prior to that, she served for 15 years as vice president and chief operating officer at Good Samaritan Hospital in Los Angeles. She currently serves on the University of Wisconsin Foundation Board, the Board of Visitors for the UW School of Nursing, and the Wise & Healthy Aging Board.

Through our combined experiences and a look at the current climate in healthcare and board governance, you will learn:

- What governance is and how boards work

- Why it is important for nurses to become involved in the governance process

- What knowledge, skills, and abilities nurses need to achieve board-level roles

- How nurses can build their knowledge, skills, and abilities

- How to seek out a position and present yourself as a board-ready candidate

Dive in! You have a lot to learn about the opportunities that await you and how you can best position yourself to be *on board*. This book begins with a discussion of what governance is, generally as well as within the healthcare realm. Then I cover what nurses, specifically, need to know about governance. I take a look at the unique benefits they can bring to board service as well as areas where they may need to further develop their skills and broaden their experiences. Finally, I take a look at what nurses need to do *now* to begin building the portfolio of skills that will position them for board service on start-up, nonprofit, advisory, and corporate boards.

Along the way, you will learn about the different types of boards, the way they work, and the types of skills and experiences they are looking for. You will learn how boards make decisions about recruiting new board members and how you can best position yourself as a candidate. And you will learn how you can develop, nurture, and leverage your personal and professional networks to ensure that you are on the radar when board roles become available.

If you have ever considered the possibility of board service, this book will give you the insights you need to gain your first board role. Even if you have already served on boards, this book will provide you with best-practice advice from seasoned board leaders that you can put to work to further the value that you bring.

> *"Apply yourself. Get all the education you can, but then, by God, do something. Don't just stand there, make it happen." –Lee Iacocca*

1

BOARD BASICS

Salaries, staffing cutbacks, clinical outcomes, adding new programs, and ending old programs all are decisions made in the boardroom. Nurses have multiple opportunities to become involved with a board of directors. A wide range of boards exist, ranging from nonprofit boards (most hospital boards are nonprofit) to corporate (for profit) boards that govern very large, publicly held organizations. There are also advisory boards, start-up boards, and nursing or professional association boards. All these types of boards share common elements; however, there are important differences.

Educate yourself about the different types of boards, as well as how your specific board operates, who the stakeholders are, and what their roles are. Then, learn your responsibilities as a board member. Other members may not instruct you fully of your roles and responsibilities, even if you become a member.

Nonprofit status means that the organization does not have to pay federal income taxes and property taxes. In exchange for their nonprofit status, organizations are expected to benefit the communities in which they serve.

UNDERSTANDING GOVERNANCE

The concept of governance has existed for hundreds of years and traces back to European countries. It is the basis for much of what we now know as corporate governance. In the case of hospital boards, governance means responsibility for the hospital's performance.

In the United States, boards have nearly always governed corporations. In fact, an 1811 New York act (Birdseye, 1890) established that "... the stock, property and concerns of such company shall be managed and conducted by trustees, who, except those for the first year, shall be elected at such time and place as shall be directed by the by-laws of the said company" (p. 1876).

Nonprofit and not-for-profit are often used interchangeably. However, for the purposes of this book, we will refer to nonprofit to indicate an organization established for purposes other than profit making and that is recognized by its government as tax exempt.

Daniel J. Pesut is a professor in the University of Minnesota–Twin Cities School of Nursing and director of the Katharine J. Densford International Center for Nursing Leadership. Pesut has a significant amount of board experience, most notably as a member of the board of directors for Sigma Theta Tau International (STTI), where he served for 8 years as a director, president-elect, and president.

"Having your finger on the pulse of what those stakeholders want is critical," says Pesut. "You can't just sit in the boardroom. You've really got to pay attention to those people you serve and figure out how to engage them in strategic ways." In other words, if you're on a hospital board, what is important to patients and staff? Board members represent the organization and are stewards of the organization, but they *serve* the stakeholders.

Gladys Campbell is the chief executive officer for the Northwest Organization of Nurse Executives (NWONE). "Many nurses really don't understand the role of a trustee," says Campbell. "Before going into a board role, we need to understand what the role of a board is and what a trustee on a board is accountable for."

Nurses considering board service need to understand both what a board does and what their role and responsibilities will be if they pursue board service. "I don't think most nurses have this information, and I don't think most boards perform a fully effective job of orienting board members to their board roles and responsibilities," says Campbell.

A board's responsibilities mostly focus on the organization; some responsibilities focus on the board itself.

Board roles and responsibilities include:

- Developing policies that provide a framework for the organization's actions and decision-making

- Setting goals that direct the chief executive officer (CEO) and the organization toward achieving specific levels of performance in areas such as financial health, quality, and safety

- Being responsible for CEO performance, setting and managing the implementation of performance goals, evaluating the outcomes, and setting CEO compensation

In general, a board's primary responsibility is to guide and direct an organization to ensure that it meets stakeholder needs.

HEALTH TRENDS

As hospitals have increasingly become part of larger systems, and independent hospitals are becoming less common, these new organizations generally have both system and local boards.

In addition, many hospitals operate foundations that are also governed by boards. Each type of healthcare board has different roles and responsibilities. Some systems operate in a centralized fashion, where most decisions are made at the systems level; others are decentralized, and local hospital boards have a great deal of autonomy. In other words, some boards work mostly by committee, and others work more as a whole board. A review of the board's charter will reveal the particular board's duties.

BOARD TYPES

Different regulations are specific to different kinds of boards: specifically, profit and nonprofit. The board members are obligated to understand the regulations that dictate their roles and responsibilities.

Boards vary greatly on the amount of time and money they expect from their board members.

The pathway to a corporate board role for nurses will likely progress from a nonprofit, or an advisory board, to a start-up and then to a corporate role. There are important lessons to be learned and experiences to be gained along this journey.

START-UP BOARDS

Like nonprofit boards, start-up boards are usually easier to gain membership on than corporate boards. Typically, start-ups are small entrepreneurial efforts—companies that are in a formative stage. The kinds of skills that these small entrepreneurial companies need are different from the kinds of skills needed in corporate governance. Yet, as these companies move from their small formative stages into more advanced stages, they can benefit from the wisdom and governance experience that a board can bring.

Start-ups are often looking for independent individuals with a variety of life experience. They cannot offer their board members much in terms of remuneration for their help, but they often offer shares of stock. If the company is a hit, board members can do well financially.

Start-up companies usually have a small, highly specialized group of employees. They rarely have support departments such as human resources. They often do not have clear policies in place, and they may need assistance with determining CEO evaluation and compensation. Very often, the CEO is one of the early entrepreneurs who founded the company. He or she may have great skills for forming a business yet lack the skills to manage and govern, especially as the organization grows. Thus, a board can provide a good complement to the entrepreneur in terms of bringing the knowledge and skills needed to make the growing business a success.

Start-up companies generally need to raise funds in order to develop. A common source of early funding is from *venture capitalists*, who invest in the organization. In exchange for this funding, the venture capitalist gets a seat on the board. This *quid pro quo* sets up an interesting and sometimes

Quid pro quo is Latin for "something for something," which means an exchange, generally for goods or services, where one "something" is contingent upon the other "something."

challenging dynamic for the board because venture capitalists seldom invest for the long term. Instead, they seek to recoup their money quickly. After repayment, they often move off the board. Thus, there are often conflicts between the short-term mentality of the venture capitalist and the focus on the long-term health of the organization that the board as a whole should be concerned. It is important that the board has representation of independent members who are there to focus on the long-term health and survival of the company.

The board needs to assist management to strategize about:

- How to build the business.

- How to build a larger customer base.

- How to please and continue to grow that customer base.

- How to revise or redevelop the product to meet the needs of emerging markets.

Nurses can be very valuable for start-up boards that:

- Seek to gain perspectives from diverse audiences.

- Are in healthcare-related industries.
  In Silicon Valley, for example, a number of start-ups produce healthcare-related apps to help monitor exercise routines, track calories, and so on. Nurses can add expertise related to the effects of chronic illness, medications, patient compliance, and others.

- Need clinical expertise, which is often highly valued by the technical development staff of start-up companies.

- Lack human resource departments or internal structure.

Nurse managers and executives bring their human resource, organizational, and leadership skills to these very technical, specialized executives and employees.

ADVISORY BOARDS

Advisory boards are different from typical boards because they do not have official decision-making responsibilities or fiduciary duties. Instead, they provide their organizations with advice and input. Advisory boards must have a clear purpose and evaluate their effectiveness in addressing that purpose.

Companies may create user groups to give them feedback on their products and services. Hospitals may have advisory boards made up of community members who share perspectives about the healthcare needs of the community. Universities often have alumni boards, which provide input for the curriculum, mentorships for graduates, and so on. Advisory boards provide a great venue for communication with stakeholders. Serving in an advisory capacity can be a good first step in learning about board service.

Laurie Benson is CEO of LSB Unlimited, a board and strategy company, and the former CEO of Inacom Information Systems. She has served on seven corporate boards in the technology, finance, insurance, manufacturing, and services industries and has been actively engaged in the healthcare industry through board service and executive leadership roles. She currently serves on five private company boards and five non-profit boards. "In my case, I found myself a founder and CEO of a technology company, yet I had no background in the field," she recalls. "What I did have was a vision for the impending importance of technology in providing information for companies to make decisions in a fast-paced and changing world." She knew that she would need wisdom from others.

"We created an advisory board from day one," she says. "We had seven advisors and three employees." Over time, she evolved this advisory board into a high-performance board of directors, but from the outset she embraced the concept of how a group of very smart people could play a key role.

HEALTHCARE TRENDS

As more independent hospitals become part of larger systems, local hospital boards become more advisory in nature. The local boards lose their fiduciary responsibilities, and the true governance exists at the system level.

In the 2013–2018 Futurescan report from the American College of Healthcare Executives (ACHE, 2013), one of the trends noted is that the economic pressures hospitals face will fuel more consolidation among systems and the elimination of local boards. The bar is rising for board members at the system level.

The report further suggests that:

- Boards will need to evolve to meet the more complex needs of the future as hospitals transform into care systems.
- Board members must be selected based on the skills and expertise they bring as well as their strategic and visionary abilities.
- Clear standards must be established for board members' attendance and participation.
- Continuing education is necessary to keep board members up to date on the rapid changes in the field.
- Boards must engage in a regular and rigorous self-assessment process.

Despite the fact that these smaller, local hospital boards are likely to diminish in terms of their governance role, they do present another opportunity for nurses hoping to gain board experience.

PROFESSIONAL NURSING ORGANIZATIONS

American nursing organizations have evolved with the nursing profession. The first U.S. nurses' training school was started in 1873 (New York University Health Sciences Library, n.d.). A mere 20 years later, the American Society of Superintendents of Training Schools for Nurses was founded (Egenes, 2009). This society was focused on helping the schools' administrators identify common curriculum, standards, policies, and procedures. The organization evolved into the National League for Nursing, which still focuses on issues related to nursing education.

Today, there are hundreds of professional nursing organizations. Some are focused on nursing scholarship, such as Sigma Theta Tau International; some are focused on specific clinical practice areas, such as the Oncology Nursing Society and the American Association of Critical-Care Nurses; some are focused on nursing education, such as the National League of Nursing; and some are broad based in their focus, such as the American Nurses Association. Despite the many differences between and among the various organizations, they all have governing boards. Many nurses report that their first governance experiences were in nursing organizations.

Nursing associations typically have local, state, regional, national, and sometimes international chapters. Many nurses join their local chapter and find it relatively easy to volunteer for a committee assignment and eventually move into a board position at a local level.

Many organizations are involved in political advocacy on the state and national level. They work to influence legislators regarding the needs of nurses and the patients who they serve. Each nursing organization has its unique mission statement, values, vision, and goals. Most nursing organizations' goals include:

- Providing a voice for nurses to influence their practice, regulations, standards, and so on

- Offering educational activities for their members

- Offering advanced certification and other types of credentials that help members advance their careers

They all have the advantages of:

- Networking

- Career assistance

- Annual conventions and meetings

- Massive databases regarding issues of evidence-based practice, best clinical practices, and so on

- Disseminating new and important data to their membership

Nursing organization boards do all the things other boards do: choose, direct, evaluate, and reward the organization's CEO; approve and monitor the budget; and focus on recruiting, retaining, and optimizing the organization's membership. Essentially, they have all the responsibilities of any non-profit board.

Nurse board members are helpful because of their stakeholder knowledge. Nurses are often close to patients and families in their professional roles, and they also interact with community members through their participation in places of faith, education, civic, and others.

Susan Groenwald is the president of Chamberlain College of Nursing in Chicago. Groenwald was elected to the board of directors of the Oncology Nursing Society in 1975. "I was a complete unknown at the time," says Groenwald, "but was director of the oncology graduate program at Rush and a charter member of the Oncology Nursing Society (ONS). My master's degree was a clinical specialist in oncology nursing from Rush." She was elected to the International Reciprocal Trade Association (IRTA) in 1983, which is an international trade association for commercial barter companies. Currently, she serves on the board of trustees of Chamberlain College of Nursing and put together the board.

"Both the ONS and IRTA were my industry associations, which were facing industry, legislative, regulatory, and quality issues that were important to me," says Groenwald. "I believed that I needed to have a voice, and needed to be a leader in solving the challenges of my industry."

The best thing nurses can do, says Groenwald, is get involved in a nursing association—join committees and volunteer to help at conventions or other initiatives. "Make yourself known and be helpful to the point of being invaluable. When the time is right, and you have paid dues and served the organization, run for office," she recommends.

HEALTHCARE TRENDS

Recently, there has been a great deal of legislative discussion regarding the scope of practice—or practice acts—of advanced practice nurses (APN). Professional nursing organizations have worked tirelessly to expand APN nursing practice acts.

FOR-PROFIT (CORPORATE) GOVERNANCE

Corporate boards exist to maximize shareholder value. A corporation's board of directors is elected by the company's shareholders. There are many specific Security and Exchange Commission (SEC) regulations that dictate how corporate boards are to function. Boards that violate these rules risk huge fines, public humiliation, and even possible incarceration for executives or board members. There have been numerous instances over the years where corporate governance has led to scandal. The Enron financial fraud scandal of 2000 led to the creation of The Sarbanes-Oxley Act in 2002 (SOX) (Fass, A., 2003). SOX governs the actions of U.S. corporate boards of directors, including the regulation requiring that the work of corporate boards become very visible and transparent. Many nonprofit boards, including hospital boards, have also applied SOX principles, although they are not required to do so. SOX mandates that members of the board's audit and compensation committees be only independent board members.

For-profit governance is often referred to as *corporate governance*. Corporate governance is the system of structure: the duties and the regulations by which corporations are directed and controlled. In corporations, *shareholders* are the owners. That's not necessarily the same as a stakeholder.

The corporate governance system in the United States is subject to a high degree of regulation. When considering, then, who should be a board member, it is important to consider those who have expertise in running a business or deep knowledge of a particular industry. Corporate boards are often made up of former CEOs and CFOs, individuals who have a high level of expertise in an area of business, experts in regulation, information systems, marketing, and so on.

Nurses seldom think of themselves as candidates for corporate boards, usually lacking experience as a CEO or CFO. However, nurses can position their backgrounds and experiences in other ways as key benefits for a board position.

Independent board members are those who have no financial relationship with the company.

Nurses can be very valuable for corporate boards because:

- Many nurse executives manage budgets that may be equivalent to the budget of a small corporation. It is not unusual for a nurse manager to have responsibility for dozens of employees.

- The financial and human resource skills needed to manage units, hospitals, and clinics are appropriate skills for board positions. Nurses who serve as deans and association executives have the financial, human resource, and customer service experience necessary for board roles.

- Nurses have deep knowledge about something that is critically important to a business. Pediatric nurses, for instance, know about baby formula or diapers. They have interacted with hundreds or even thousands of parents, and they have been privy to their perspectives. Diaper or formula companies could receive significant benefit from those insights.

When I was at Montefiore Medical Center 30 years ago, I managed a budget of $130 million and had 2,500 RNs within my organization. Montefiore had 10,000 employees in ancillary, housekeeping, dietary, and other roles.

Few individuals outside healthcare realize the budget and human resource responsibilities that nurses possess. Highlighting those responsibilities on resumes and letters of introduction is essential.

We had numerous union contracts, a medical school, and thousands of physicians. We were a complex organization of hospitals, clinics, and homecare settings. In the 1980s, there were many American companies that were smaller than my nursing organization at Montefiore.

Still, where most nurses will gain access to a corporate board is not through budget management or high-level corporate positions.

CASE STUDY

Pyxis, Inc., was the first corporate board that I served on as a board member. Pyxis is a company that provides technology related to medication supply and safety pioneered an automated medication-dispensing system. When I was a practicing clinical nurse, one of my key interests was getting patients their medications on time. Back then, a number of barriers interfered with timely medication administration. It was often necessary to leave your patients and run to the hospital pharmacy, or the pharmacist would have to run up to the unit, or you'd have to get a last-minute order from a physician—and it seemed nearly impossible to get in touch with a physician or pharmacist when you needed an urgent medication order.

So, when I saw that first Pyxis device and found that the meds would be on the unit—and when the nurse inserted her PIN, she had immediate access to the patient's medication—I became a huge fan of the technology. For a number of years, I encouraged that company to just keep pushing that technology, and I supported and encouraged the company and talked about Pyxis whenever I could. It was such a wonderful thing for nurses and physicians, and it saved patients from suffering. I watched as other healthcare organizations installed the product, and it became obvious that Pyxis saved enormous amounts of time for nurses and pharmacists and enabled patients to receive their medications in a timely manner.

At one point, Pyxis offered to pay me for my support and promotion of its technology, but I didn't feel right about getting paid, so I said to Pyxis, "I'd like to be on your board." Even I was surprised that I said that, but I had been on a couple of nonprofit boards, and I realized how much power a board can exert on the product. In a hospital, the product is patient care; for Pyxis, the product was this medication-dispensing system.

I caught the CEO by surprise when I asked to be on the board, and he told me that the board was entirely filled with venture capitalists that had given Pyxis money. But he assured me that when one of those investors was repaid and left the board, he would put me on it, and he did.

The day he introduced me to the other board members, who were all brilliant men with financial backgrounds, he said, "Connie is the only one of you who has ever been in touch with the people who use our product. She knows how it benefits nurses, pharmacists, and patients." That was my key differentiator for this board, and that's what made me valuable to them. That's what can also make you valuable to various boards. It's something you need to really think about in terms of how you build your resume to position yourself for board service.

It was my academic background that appealed to the DeVry Education Group board members. DeVry was diversifying into the healthcare professions and wanted to find a board member who understood academic healthcare organizations and nursing education. Earlier in my career, I was a faculty member at several universities and Dean at the Medical College of Wisconsin. The DeVry board valued my nursing and academic background and selected me to serve on its board.

Linda Procci, PhD, RN, was vice president for Service Line Operations at Cedars-Sinai Medical Center in Los Angeles. "Most of the boards that I've been on have been small, nonprofit boards with budgets of $15 million a year, or less, and a very focused mission," says Procci. For example, she has also served on the Los Angeles Free Clinic board, which, she says, "exemplifies the kind of board opportunities that are out there for nurses."

Procci stresses that a nursing perspective can be readily applied in any type of boardroom setting. "Nursing can be practiced anywhere, so it would be hard for me to imagine any organization where your health-care clinical skill would not come into play," she says. For instance, "If your organization has employees, at the very least they're going to be discussing selecting the right health insurance plan for their employees. They may be dealing with safety issues and workers compensation issue." These are topics that nurses are well positioned to discuss.

As you study the organization's mission and goals, identify how your personal and professional experience can contribute to the organization's success.

What experiences have you had with consumers—or patients—that provide you with keen insights that would make you a valuable member of a corporate board? How can you quantify those experiences in your resume?

NONPROFIT GOVERNANCE

Nonprofit organizations have stakeholders rather than shareholders. Stakeholders are the *owners*—individuals who are significantly affected by the organization. They are individuals or groups who have important wants and needs that they rely on an organization to meet. They are invested in a way other than monetarily. By and large, hospitals are nonprofit companies. Nursing organizations are nonprofit organizations. Board members act like stakeholders would if they were guiding and governing the organization.

Members on nonprofits boards are stakeholder advocates.

HEALTHCARE TRENDS

Healthcare organizations specifically have stakeholders that include citizens, patients, employees, physicians, and many others. Usually, a hospital board's core responsibility is related to providing high-quality, cost-effective healthcare.

The Guide to Not-for-Profit Governance (Weil, Gotshal & Manges, LLP, 2012), sponsored by the Not-for-Profit Practice Group and the Pro Bono Committee of Weil, Gotshal & Manges LLP, notes that

> The role of the board of directors of a not-for-profit organization is similar to the role of a for-profit board. In both cases, the organizations are tasked with managing other people's money and in both cases they are judged by their success in doing so. Yet, there is a very key difference: in the for-profit context, shareholders are able to hold corporate directors and officers accountable, whereas in the not-for-profit context there is no private mechanism by which the organization can be held accountable when it fails to act in furtherance of its mission (pp. 1-2).

Nonprofit organizations typically have many stakeholders, often with conflicting needs. Board members must have a range of knowledge, skills, and behaviors to govern effectively on the stakeholders' behalves.

Know who your organization's stakeholders are. Know what they most expect and need from the organization.

Because stakeholders and their needs can change over time, boards should conduct periodic stakeholder assessments to stay updated. Stakeholders judge the organization based on how well the board meets its needs and expectations. They also seek care (or whatever "product" they get from the organization) elsewhere if their needs are not met.

HEALTHCARE TRENDS

Consider a small community that is about a 20-minute drive from a larger city. For years, the stakeholders of the hospital located in the small community have rated cost and quality of care as their key concerns. A large corporation recently established its headquarters in the larger, nearby city. The corporation is attracting a large number of younger employees. Many of these employees and their families are moving to the smaller community because it is a good place to raise a family relatively close to their work.

In addition to affordable, quality care, these young people want greater access to care at more locations and at times that are convenient for them. These new younger families have integrated technology into their daily lives. They want to work with clinicians whom they can e-mail their questions and receive a timely response. They want easy and rapid access to clinicians at "minute clinics" and other ambulatory centers. They want immediate access to their medical records and key healthcare information. What was once a 20-minute geographic advantage for the older, small community hospital disappears in an age of technology.

Thus, the stakeholder dynamic is changing for the hospital board based on the influx of these young families and their needs. For these families, if their questions can be answered through e-mail and there is easy, rapid, ambulatory access, they have no need to affiliate with a healthcare organization merely because of physical proximity.

HOW CORPORATE AND NONPROFIT BOARDS DIFFER

For-profit boards and nonprofit boards are the two major board classifications:

- **For-profit boards** are associated with corporations and are owned by their stockholders. Their chief purpose is to increase stockholder wealth. Corporate boards are usually small, and their board members are paid.

- **Nonprofit organizations** are usually owned by the community and exist to serve a community need. These boards are usually large and made up of unpaid volunteers.

Table 1.1 shows some clear distinctions between for-profit and nonprofit organizations.

TABLE 1.1: COMPARING CORPORATE AND NONPROFIT BOARDS

Corporate Boards	Nonprofit Boards
They're owned by stockholders.	They're owned by the public (stakeholders).
They generate money for the owners.	They serve the public/constituents.
Success is making sizeable profit.	Success is meeting the needs of the public/constituents.
Board members are usually paid.	Board members are usually unpaid volunteers.
Money earned over and above what is needed to pay expenses is kept as profit and distributed to shareholders.	Money earned over and above that needed to pay expenses is retained as surplus and spent on meeting public need (essential to keeping tax-free status).

continues

TABLE 1.1: COMPARING CORPORATE AND NONPROFIT BOARDS   (CONTINUED)

Corporate Boards	Nonprofit Boards
The CEO is often on the board of directors and is sometimes the chairperson of the board.	The CEO is not usually a board member but attends board meetings.
They pay federal, state, and local taxes.	They're usually exempt from paying federal, state, and local taxes.
Money invested in for-profits typically cannot be deducted from the investor's personal tax liability.	Money donated to the nonprofit can be deducted from the donor's personal tax liability (if the nonprofit was granted charitable status from the appropriate government agency).

Adapted from McNamara, C. (2008). *Field guide to developing, operating, and restoring your nonprofit board.* Authenticity Consulting, LLC: Minneapolis, MN.

TRANSPARENCY AND PROXY STATEMENTS

Both nonprofit and corporate boards have rules that board members must understand and comply with. In the profit world, one of these compliance areas is transparency.

The proxy statement includes both good news and sometimes not-so-good news. A proxy statement is required when firms are soliciting shareholder votes, and it is filed with the SEC in advance of the corporation's annual meeting.

In the proxy statement, the corporation is required to include details about the past year's business performance and activities anticipated for the future. Any expected changes of a material—or major—nature need to be conveyed. These might include such things as losing a big contract, acquiring another

Transparency means being forthright with the truth regarding all aspects of organizational operations. Transparency is formalized in a *proxy statement*, which is a thorough document that presents the state of the company.

organization, and so on. Basically, any event that could impact the value and the performance of the company over the next year should be discussed in the proxy statement.

To review a proxy statement, find a sample online. In one Apple, Inc. proxy statement, for instance, the company sought approval on:

- Electing representatives to the board

- Amending the "blank check" authority of the board to issue preferred stock

- Approving the employee stock ownership plan

These are the types of things that Apple shareholders would review and determine whether to vote for or against—or whether to allow their votes to be handled by proxy.

Although proxy statements exist in the world of corporate governance, best-practice nonprofit organizations provide transparency to their stakeholders, too. Many hospitals provide an annual community benefit report to inform their stakeholders of their many charitable activities.

The term *proxy* also refers to voting. When you own shares in a company, you have the right to vote those shares. If you cannot be physically present at a shareholder meeting, you might allow your shares to be voted on by *proxy*. That is, by someone else.

INDEPENDENCE

For members of corporate boards and nonprofit boards, the issue of independence is becoming increasingly important.

Here, again, is an area where nurses have an advantage. Being independent means that you do not have a financial relationship with the company and that nobody in your immediate family has a financial relationship with the company. True financial independence eliminates many conflicts of interest. Board members who are responsible for the organization's audit and executive compensation are much more likely to make fair and responsible decisions if they are not financially related to the organization.

The SEC requires that all members of a corporate board's audit or compensation committees be independent. This same type of requirement is emerging in the nonprofit sector.

BOARD MEMBER COMPENSATION

Corporate boards are paid for board service. Compensation is usually a combination of a cash retainer and shares of stock, often 50/50, with half cash retainer and half shares of stock.

Nonprofit board members usually are not paid. This is changing, however. Still, the pay for board members in the nonprofit arena, when they are paid, is significantly less than what directors receive in the for-profit world.

HEALTHCARE TRENDS

Compensation for nonprofit hospital board members is on the rise. In its 2013 survey of hospitals and healthcare systems, the Governance Institute found that the percentage of nonprofit hospitals and health systems that compensated some or all of their board members increased from 10.2% in 2009 to 15.5% in 2013. This trend is expected to continue because healthcare organizations are dealing with increasing complexity that demands a higher level of expertise and engagement among board members.

According to Green and Suzuki (2013), pay for directors of the Standard & Poor's 500 Index (SPX) rose to a record average of $251,000 in 2012. That was the sixth consecutive year that board compensation increased. For their compensation, board members work an average of 250 to 300 hours per year. According to the same article, the lowest paying board is Berkshire Hathaway, which should come as no surprise given Warren Buffett's reputation for frugality. Buffett, Berkshire Hathaway's famous CEO, pays his board members only $3,800 per year, but he also gives them shares of stock, which is common, and incredibly valuable in this particular case. Tyson Foods is at the high end with an average board member cash retainer of $540,000.

Because shareholding is an effective way to align the interests of the board, the executives, the employees, and the public, there are many shareholding requirements. It is generally believed to be in the best interest of shareholders if corporate directors own shares of stock. If share values increase, the directors and shareholders benefit together. If share prices go down, both are negatively impacted. Members of the corporation's management and executive team are also expected to own shares of stock. Many corporations expect executives to own shares equal to a multiple of their annual compensation.

For-profit board members are generally required to own a certain number of shares over a certain period of time. Thus, typically, there would be a requirement at the end of 5 years to be holding a certain number of shares, at least equal in value to the board member's annual compensation. These shares are not given to the board member and must be purchased at their expense—with most requiring board members maintaining a specific share level.

THE BOARD'S FIDUCIARY ROLE AND BOARD MEMBER DUTIES

Understanding your role as a board member is crucial to performing your duties effectively.

A fiduciary can have legal duties. That person, per *Slee's Healthcare Terms* (2007), acts primarily for another person's benefit. It is incorrect to believe that a board's fiduciary role extends only to its financial oversight responsibilities. In fact, the board's fiduciary responsibilities go beyond financial.

The issue of quality is relevant to any board setting, of course. For instance, in the academic world, the board is responsible for ensuring the quality of the academic product and the viability of the university.

The DeVry Education Group uses a scorecard that measures academic achievement, student persistence, faculty engagement, and other key metrics that address the fiduciary responsibilities of its various academic boards. In professional associations, the board will be focused on ensuring the quality of the services provided to its members. In corporations, the board is responsible for the quality of the product or services that it sells.

Fiduciary is related to trust, especially when someone benefits and someone else is in charge (a *trustee*). Although most individuals who serve on boards today are referred to as *board members* or *directors,* the more traditional term is *board of trustees* and *trustee.* That language speaks to the critical importance of the board's fiduciary role.

HEALTHCARE TRENDS

A board's fiduciary responsibilities include oversight of areas such as organizational compliance with legal and regulatory requirements; and in the case of hospital or health system boards, the areas of quality of care and patient safety.

In recent years, there has been a much greater emphasis placed on the boards' responsibilities around patient safety and quality. For the first time in U.S. history, the Centers for Medicare & Medicaid Services (n.d.) pay hospitals based on the quality of performance. Board members are expected to know how the healthcare organization measures and monitors quality. They are expected to establish quality goals and discuss them at every board meeting.

In the case of healthcare organizations, it is important to have quality goals for patient outcomes, patient satisfaction, and employee and physician satisfaction as well as the health of the community. Nurses are well positioned here. Healthcare boards are looking for people who have experience with quality outcomes, satisfaction, and healthcare metrics.

Regardless of the type of organization, board members have legal duties that they must perform.

THE DUTY OF CARE

The Duty of Care is focused on the board's process of decision-making. The Revised Model Nonprofit Corporation Act of 1987, which guided the development of many state laws, the first of the board's core legal duties—the Duty of Care—requires board members to:

- Act in good faith

- Use the same degree of diligence, care, and skill that a prudent person would use in similar circumstances

The Duty of Care focuses on *how* trustees act and make decisions rather than on the *results* of their actions or decisions.

- Act in a manner that the director reasonably believes to be in the best interests of the corporation (Siegel, 2006)

Board members must meet the following essential requirements to fulfill the Duty of Care (p. 82):

- **Make informed decisions** by being diligent and prudent, using good judgment, and exercising a reasonable effort to become familiar with relevant, available facts. This, of course, requires that board members do their homework and attend all board meetings.

- **Conduct due inquiry.** That is, they must ask questions if facts raise issues about the validity and completeness of the information the board receives. It is important that board members thoroughly discuss and debate issues. When members always vote unanimously, it looks like a "rubber stamp board" rather than a conscientious group of decision-makers. Often, closed executive sessions are called to allow discussion to build board cohesiveness for a show of solidarity, especially for controversial decisions.

According to governance expert Dennis Pointer (Pointer, 2008), the test for determining whether the Duty of Care has been fulfilled is to ask the question, "Is there evidence that reasonable care was exercised?" The test is not, "Was the result optimal, satisfactory, or even tolerable?"

Pointer says that directors, for example, can presume that data, analyses, and recommendations from others are accurate and truthful if there appears to be no evidence to the contrary. He also says that the Duty of Care does not require board members to be overly cautious or to avoid taking any risks. What they must do is be informed and act carefully with good sense and sound judgment.

Most state courts offer trustees further protection through the business judgment rule, which provides that trustees will not be held personally liable if they make informed decisions, in good faith, without self-interest and in the best interest of the corporation. It is critical to know the laws. The courts will not protect trustees who claim ignorance while making no effort to understand the laws.

There are many actions that board members can take to fulfill the Duty of Care:

- Be prepared for all board and committee meetings.

- Ask questions or seek additional information.

- Ensure that the organization has in place and has implemented an effective compliance plan.

- Be aware of quality and safety trends and how the organization continues to improve its quality and safety performance.

- Challenge assumptions and ensure alternatives were satisfactorily explored before accepting recommendations.

- Be willing to express a dissenting opinion or negative vote when they believe it is the right thing to do.

THE DUTY OF LOYALTY

The Duty of Loyalty requires board members to safeguard the organization's business interests. Fulfilling the Duty of Loyalty means that board members understand they owe allegiance to the organization's stakeholders and act in the stakeholders' best interests (Entin, Andersen, & O'Brien, 2006).

To fulfill the duty of loyalty, board members must:

- *Act in good faith and without self-interest when making decisions*

- *Preserve the confidentiality of corporate affairs*

  They cannot discuss confidential board deliberations or actions outside the boardroom.

- *Avoid conflicts of interest*

  Board members should understand that in today's world, best-practice organizations are beginning to hold themselves to a higher standard with regard to conflicts of interest and are seeking individuals who are not conflicted to serve on the board.

- *Avoid taking advantage of a corporate opportunity for personal gain*

  That requires disclosing all conflicts of interest at least annually by completing a conflict-of-interest statement and acknowledging before the board any conflicts that may come throughout the year. Many organizations now ask board members to disclose all affiliations annually so the determination of conflict of interest falls to the board and not the board member.

Board members must understand that considerable questions have been raised about whether a board member who has an interest in a business that competes with the organization can adequately fulfill his or her Duty of Loyalty. At the same time, this does not mean that a person with a conflict of interest is automatically prevented from serving on a board.

However, when a conflict is present, conditions must be met. These conditions include:

Because of the vast number of nurses in a community, it is relatively easy to find nurse board members who are truly independent, with no financial relationship with a healthcare organization.

- Making sure the board is given notice in advance that it will be considering an issue in conflict

- Identifying the director who has the conflict

- Asking the conflicted director to leave the room while the board deliberates and votes on the issue

HEALTHCARE TRENDS

Many healthcare organizations are changing their structures to resemble accountable care organizations (ACOs) or other structures that include employing or partnering with physicians. As an employee, a physician is not an independent trustee. The same is true for anyone who is an employee of the organization or has a business relationship with it. These new organizational structures are provoking organizations to re-examine their board policies and relationships. The many changes in organizational structure and governance provide a good opportunity for nurses to seek board positions.

THE DUTY OF OBEDIENCE

The Duty of Obedience requires board members to comply with applicable laws, rules, and regulations. The Duty of Obedience is the most important duty. If an organization's board does not obey the laws and comply with regulations, the Duties of Loyalty and Care are irrelevant.

To fulfill the Duty of Obedience (Hopt & von Hippel, 2010), board members must:

What happens in the board room stays in the boardroom, down to the smallest details.

- Honor the terms and conditions of the organization's mission, bylaws, policies, and procedures

- Act at all times within the scope of their authority under the corporation's articles, bylaws, and applicable laws

There's no place for social media in the boardroom.

29

- In nonprofit organizations, focus beyond the organization's financial health to safeguard its charitable purpose

- Preserve the organization's assets held in trust for the community

Boards can comply with the Duty of Obedience by:

- *Instructing new and seasoned board members about the requirements of this duty and how to fulfill them*

- *Ensuring that all board members understand key laws and regulations and their implications for organizational governance*

- *Keeping an up-to-date book of board policies and procedures*

  Many organizations are now putting their policies and procedures online so that they can consistently and easily be updated.

- *Educating the board about changes and ensuring that the board does not act in ways that are inconsistent with them*

  It is the responsibility of the board to pursue continuing education about the changing rules and regulations that affect their organization.

VISION, MISSION, AND VALUES

One of a board's key responsibilities is to establish (or revisit at regular intervals) the organization's vision.

Vision statements are usually broad, inspiring, and future focused. As such, their language is typically high level and lacks specific details.

Vision statements describe what an organization is striving to become in order to meet stakeholder needs and expectations.

Vision statements should be challenging enough to guide the organization for many years.

Consider the vision statement of Dignity Health, a California-based nonprofit healthcare system that operates hospitals and ancillary care facilities in 17 states. From its early inception, Dignity Health envisioned itself as, "a growing and diversified healthcare ministry distinguished by excellent quality and committed to expanding access to those in need." Consider what this vision statement tells you about the organization. What stakeholder needs does the Dignity Health vision say the system is committed to meeting today and into the future?

Mission statements can guide organizations to meaningful strategies and goals. They should energize stakeholders and position the organization as unique.

Flowing from its vision to be a ministry focused on quality of and access to healthcare, the mission of Dignity Health stated: "Dignity Health and our Sponsoring Congregations are committed to furthering the healing ministry of Jesus. We dedicate our resources to: Delivering compassionate, high-quality affordable health services, serving and advocating for our sisters and brothers who are poor and disenfranchised, partnering with others in the community to improve the quality of life." This mission statement is clear about the organization's commitment to its religious foundations; high-quality, affordable care; and focusing on the poor and disenfranchised.

Mission statements describe the primary work of the organization today, not the future, in service of stakeholder needs and expectations.

Values statements describe the core behaviors that guide stakeholder relationships, defining how the organization will act.

Values statements are consistent with the mission and vision. As such, they should drive action that supports them. For example, an organization's values should help focus hiring decisions that result in employees who share the organization's values. They should reward behavior consistent with them. It is important for board members and leaders to understand that their behavior must reflect the values to ensure that others in the organization behave in ways that support the values as well.

Dignity Health expressed its foundational values in the following way: "Dignity Health is committed to providing high-quality affordable healthcare to the communities we serve. Above all, we value:

- *Dignity*—respecting the inherent value and worth of each person

- *Collaboration*—working together with people who support common values and vision to achieve shared goals

- *Justice*—advocating for social change and acting in ways that promote respect for all persons and demonstrate compassion for our sisters and brothers who are powerless

- *Stewardship*—cultivating the resources entrusted to us to promote healing and wholeness

- *Excellence*—exceeding expectations through teamwork and innovation."

Even though these values may seem similar to those of other healthcare organizations, it is often in the values statement that the organization's unique identity is clearly expressed.

To gain a better understanding of this, compare the Dignity Health values statement (Dignity Health, n.d.) with the values of the Carolinas HealthCare System, which expresses its four core values in this way.

"Carolinas HealthCare System recognizes our employees are our most valuable asset. We have identified four core values successful employees need to strive for in order for us to accomplish our mission:

- Caring: We treat our customers with dignity, giving them the courtesy and gentleness they need. We are helpful; we listen; we communicate; we respond to patient needs.

- Commitment: We are dedicated to Carolinas HealthCare System, taking pride in our organization and our jobs, projecting a professional image, and striving to be the best in all we do.

- Integrity: We honor and uphold confidentiality, are honest and ethical, keep our commitments, accept responsibility for our actions, and respect the rights of patients, families, and each other.

- Teamwork: Linked by our common mission, we respect the professionalism and contributions of our coworkers, understand that physicians are an integral part of the team, value diversity in all its forms, and recognize that people are our greatest asset.

The Carolinas HealthCare System core values are different from that of Dignity Health and express the foundational beliefs, which guide this system to achieve its mission and vision. The type of board member, executive, or employee attracted to one system may not be attracted to the other.

REFERENCES

American College of Healthcare Executives (ACHE). (2013). *Futurescan 2013: Healthcare trends and implications 2013–2018.* Author. Chicago, IL. http://www.ache.org/publications/Product.aspx?pc=2243

Birdseye, C. F. (1890). *The revised statutes, codes and general laws of the state of New York to January first 1890.* https://books.google.com/books?id=II1CAQAAMAAJ&printsec=frontcover&source=gbs_ge_summary_r&cad=0#v=onepage&q&f=false

Carolinas HealthCare System. (n.d.). Mission & values. http://www.carolinashealthcare.org/chs-mission-and-values

Centers for Medicare & Medicaid Services. (n.d.). Accountable care organizations. Retrieved from http://www.cms.gov/Medicare/Medicare-Fee-for-Service-Payment/ACO/index.html?redirect=/ACO/

Egenes, K. J. (2009). History of nursing. In G. Roux and J. A. Halstead (eds.), *Issues and trends in nursing: Essential knowledge for today and tomorrow.* Burlington, MA: Jones & Bartlett Learning.

Entin, F., Andersen, J. & O'Brien, , K. (2006). *The board's fiduciary role: Legal responsibilities of health care governing boards.* Center for Healthcare Governance: Chicago, IL.

Fass, A. (July 22, 2003). One year later, the impact of Sarbanes-Oxley. *Forbes.* http://www.forbes.com/2003/07/22/cz_af_0722sarbanes.html

The Governance Institute. (2013). *Governing the value journey: A profile of structure, culture, and practices of boards in transition.* 2013 Biennial Survey of Hospitals and Healthcare Systems. Author. http://library.governanceinstitute.com/ResearchPublications/ResourceLibrary/tabid/185/CategoryID/3/List/1/Level/a/ProductID/1419/Default.aspx?SortField=DateCreated+DESC%2CDateCreated+DESC

Green, J. & Suzuki, H. (2013). Board director pay hits record $251,000 for 250 hours. *Bloomberg News.* http://www.bloomberg.com/news/2013-05-30/board-director-pay-hits-record-251-000-for-250-hours.html

Hopt, K. J. & von Hippel, T. (2010). *Comparative corporate governance of non-profit organizations.* Cambridge University Press: Cambridge, UK.

McNamara, C. (2008). *Field guide to developing, operating, and restoring your nonprofit board.* Authenticity Consulting, LLC: Minneapolis, MN

New York University Health Sciences Library. (n.d.). Bellevue School of Nursing in Lillian & Clarence de la Chapelle Medical Archives. http://archives.med.nyu.edu/collections/bellevue-school-nursing

Pointer, Dennis. (2008). *Navigating the boardroom.* Greenlake Press: Seattle, WA.

Siegel, J. B. (2006). *A desktop guide for nonprofit directors, officers, and advisors.* John Wiley & Sons: Hoboken, NJ.

Slee, D. A. & Slee, V. N. (2007). *Slee's healthcare terms.* Jones & Bartlett Learning. Sudbury, MA.

Weil, Gotshal, & Manges, LLP. (2012). *The guide to not-for-profit governance.* Author. http://www.weil.com/~/media/files/pdfs/nfpguide_2012.pdf

2

HOSPITAL GOVERNANCE TRENDS

The changes that are impacting healthcare now, and that will continue to impact the industry for some time, are demanding a closer look at the role of the board and its members.

In January 2014, *Becker's Hospital Review* published an article (Gamble, 2014) outlining 10 trends for hospital and health system governance. It included:

- The fiduciary duty for standard of care will become more rigorous.
- Boards will need an increased level of engagement from their members.
- A key responsibility for boards will be active participation in strategic planning.

- The director nomination process will become more focused on candidates who have competencies in areas such as population health, insurance capabilities, healthcare IT, and quality.

- Boards will become involved in more vigorous compliance oversight.

- Boards will partner with management to create more rigorous communication mechanisms to monitor and report on risks.

- Governance structures will be evaluated in terms of board size, composition, committee structure, reporting relationships, and reserved powers.

- There will be heightened involvement of the board and greater board ownership.

- There will be an increased focus on the risks related to new health system business initiatives.

- The role of the general counsel will become more important.

Jim Gauss, MHA, is chair of board services at Witt/Kieffer, a national executive search firm. Executive search firms are specialized recruitment services that are used to source candidates for senior, executive, or highly specialized positions in an organization. Although Gauss has years of experience in executive search, he is now focused on recruiting for healthcare organization boards. He says that hospitals are looking for board members who "know the power of asking the right question at the right time." A balance must be struck here, of course. He adds that it's important that board members neither get overly involved with the day-to-day responsibilities of the staff of the organization nor sit too quietly.

Nurses are well positioned to serve, he says, because:

- They have both technical expertise and personal maturity.

- They demonstrate independence and objectivity.

- They're *out of community*, meaning they come from a different
  community or environment that
  would provide the board with
  "greater diversity of thought, gender, and ethnicity."

Diversity, especially gender
and ethnic, is increasingly
important in an environment
where stakeholders are increasingly diverse.

STAKEHOLDERS

Hospitals have many stakeholders. Some are obvious, such as patients
and their families, or the hospital's employees and medical staff. Others,
such as legislators and regulators, are less obvious. Regardless, they have
a vested interest in the organization's success and how well it performs.

For example, religious orders or congregations sponsor some nonprofit
hospitals. The religious order is an important stakeholder of the hospital
and usually reserves the right to make decisions on important matters,
such as significant financial expenditures, who sits on the hospital's
board of directors, or their charitable mission.

ACCOUNTABILITY

Governance reforms mandated by the Sarbanes-Oxley Act of 2002
(SOX; legislation governing for-profit companies) are now finding
their way into the nonprofit sector as well. State attorneys general have

increased their focus on nonprofits and are conducting more careful reviews of issues such as chief executive officer (CEO) compensation, use of charitable assets, community benefit, and tax exemption.

These challenges are impacting the way stakeholders feel about healthcare organizations. What does that mean for board members?

The American Hospital Association's (AHA) Blue Ribbon Panel on Health Care Governance (2007) stated that,

> All health care organizations must have the trust of their many publics to survive and achieve their individual missions. And it is the governing board of a health care organization that is ultimately accountable for maintaining the public's trust, whether its members are appointed, elected, self-perpetuating, volunteer, or paid. Every other responsibility that a board has flows from this fundamental accountability and is best understood in this context (p. 6).

There are many ways that healthcare boards can be accountable to stakeholders and maintain their trust. The AHA's Blue Ribbon Panel on Health Care Governance suggests that boards and leaders can do the following:

- Be a voice for stakeholders and advocate on their behalf

- Ensure a working environment that attracts and retains the best employees

- Maintain productive working relationships with physicians

- Be mindful of open, honest, and supportive working relationships

- Ensure performance transparency

- Identify performance areas

- Conduct assessments

The following sections provide more details of these key accountabilities.

BE A VOICE FOR STAKEHOLDERS AND ADVOCATE ON THEIR BEHALF

This is a board's purpose for being. A board can work toward accomplishing this by doing the following:

- Ensuring stakeholders' needs and expectations are taken into account

- Managing management and clinical decision-making and clinical decision-making

- Setting the organization's vision, mission, and strategic goals

- Participating in political advocacy at local, state, and national levels to ensure lawmakers know what hospital stakeholders need and expect in terms of their healthcare

ENSURE A WORKING ENVIRONMENT THAT ATTRACTS AND RETAINS THE BEST EMPLOYEES

This goal is part of meeting stakeholder needs. Leading hospitals, such as the Bronson Healthcare Group in Kalamazoo, Michigan, have taken several steps to become an Employer of Choice in their community. Activities include leadership development, organization and career enhancement, communication and feedback, financial incentives and rewards, measuring and monitoring employee satisfaction, ensuring a healthy, productive workforce, employee education, and a management mentoring program.

MAINTAIN PRODUCTIVE WORKING RELATIONSHIPS WITH PHYSICIANS

Such relationships are another area of opportunity where boards and leaders can have significant impact.

Compacts provide all parties with a clear understanding of what they are responsible for and what they can expect from the other party.

Hospitals are developing written compacts between themselves and their physicians. These compacts typically spell out both the hospitals' and physicians' responsibilities and clarify the relationship.

BE MINDFUL OF OPEN, HONEST, AND SUPPORTIVE WORKING RELATIONSHIPS

According to the Blue Ribbon Panel (AHA, 2007),

> Good boards pay attention to, work at, and really assess how well the board functions together as a team, challenging one another, raising and debating several points of view and alternative courses of action, gaining information and knowledge about how the organization works and is viewed by stakeholders, and holding individuals and the full board accountable for performance (p. 12).

The CEO is usually the board's only direct report.

ENSURE PERFORMANCE TRANSPARENCY

Publicly reporting on the organization's financial, quality, and safety outcomes, as well as on the level of community benefit that the organization provides, can help give stakeholders a clearer sense of how well the organization is meeting their needs and expectations. Chapter 1, "Board Basics," explains transparency.

IDENTIFY PERFORMANCE AREAS

Use a balanced scorecard (http://balancedscorecard.org/Resources/
About-the-Balanced-Scorecard) or other reporting tool to help identify
areas of organizational performance—such as quality, safety, and
finance—that the board and leadership must monitor to meet stakeholder needs.

Organizing board and management reporting around stakeholder needs
helps ensure that they are kept front and center in organizational governance and leadership.

CONDUCT ASSESSMENTS

Periodic assessments confirm or identify new stakeholders and
understand their most important current needs and concerns. Then
board members can put stakeholder feedback to work on behalf of the
organization.

BOARD COMMITTEES

In addition to meeting as a whole, boards have committees that focus on
specific areas. They report to the full board on their activities.

All board members are expected to
serve on at least one board committee.
This requirement provides an opportunity for individuals to use their skills in
a particular area of interest, as well as to
learn about new aspects of board governance. Board service is a process of
continuous learning and personal and
professional development.

No one comes to their first
board role with all the knowledge, skills, and abilities they
need to succeed. Nurses are
no exception.

Common healthcare board committees are Audit and Finance, Quality, Compensation, and Governance/Nominating.

AUDIT AND FINANCE COMMITTEE

The organization may have separate Audit and Finance committees or may combine the two. Audit and Finance committees are responsible to the board for:

- Formulating the organization's financial objectives
- Ensuring that management's plans and budgets are aligned with board-specified financial objectives
- Monitoring financial performance and outcomes
- Ensuring that proper internal controls, such as financial processes and reporting, are in place

FINANCES

Hospitals have significant expenditures for:

- Acquiring physician practices
- Building ambulatory care centers
- Merging with other healthcare organizations
- Marketing the new entities
- Exceeding at pay for performance to generate the revenue needed for these expenditures

The members of the Finance committee must discuss, debate, and make recommendations to the entire board on the financial implications of these decisions.

Like all board work, this requires high-level, strategic consideration. For example, if one of the goals of the organization is to become the number-one cardiac care provider in the area, the budget needs to align with this goal in terms of including expenditures for the necessary staff, equipment, facilities, and so on, as well as the anticipated revenue from these activities.

AUDITS

Members of the Audit committee must be truly *independent,* meaning that they must not be engaged in any type of work for the hospital. So, for instance, a local banker who works at the bank where the hospital does its business should not be on the Audit committee. Be sure to verify the following:

- *Are the auditors independent, without any favorable relationship with management?* They should have a totally objective relationship, and they should report to the board. The Audit committee recommends to the board which audit firm to select. The annual decision about who will audit is a board—not a management—decision.

- *How will we evaluate that firm and how much will we pay for audit services?*

- *Who will be audited?* The Audit committee confers with both the auditors and management to determine this. Will they audit the entire organization, including subsidiaries such as ambulatory care clinics, home care, or nursing homes? Typically, the specific

Federal rules require Audit committee members to be truly independent, having no personal, family, or business relationship with either nonprofit or corporate governance.

elements of the audit vary annually with input from management and the Audit committee, with final approval by the board.

The Audit committee will also:

- Review all financial information before sending to external parties, such as:
    - Quarterly reports to Medicaid
    - The state
    - Various accrediting agencies and organizations
    - The Joint Commission (TJC)
- Review external auditors' opinions and share these opinions with the board
- Make recommendations to the board about how any deficiencies that are noted as part of these audits will be corrected

GOVERNANCE/NOMINATING COMMITTEE

The Governance/Nominating committee typically oversees board effectiveness. Its responsibilities include:

- Development and oversight of a criteria-based board composition process
- Development and oversight of a new board member identification
- Recruitment and orientation processes
- Development and oversight of a process to evaluate board member performance and to make reappointment recommendations

- Formulation of draft annual board goals and objectives for recommendation to the full board

- Development and oversight of a board evaluation process

- Development and oversight of a criteria-based board and committee composition process

Additional committee responsibilities include:

- Recommendation of a committee structure to the full board

- Oversight of annual board committee work plans for recommendation to the full board

- Administration of an annual evaluation process for each board committee

- Development of a criteria-based process for nominating board officers

- Development, recommendation, and evaluation of board policies and procedures

- Board education planning

NURSES IN GOVERNANCE ROLES

Nurses bring a perspective to the table that few others have. Even the physicians who serve on healthcare boards do not have the extent, or intensity, of patient interaction that nurses have.

Susan Hassmiller is the Robert Wood Johnson Foundation Senior Advisor for Nursing and Director of the Future of Nursing: Campaign for Action. She is one of the nurses driving up the number of nurses serving in governance roles. The majority of Hassmiller's board

service has been with the American Red Cross, a nonprofit. She is
the immediate past chair of the board in New Jersey and was on the
national board of governors for 6 years, chairing its disaster services
during September 11 (2001), Hurricane Katrina, and the Indian Ocean
tsunami. Most recently, Hassmiller stepped into a role as a trustee for
a large integrated health system, a new experience as this health board
comprises almost all males, and she represents not just one of only a few
female perspectives but also the only nursing perspective. That scenario
is not all that uncommon. It will be a new learning experience both
for her and for the current board, she says, stressing the importance of
having someone on a health system board that understands so clearly
how the system works.

All too often, notes Hassmiller, boards do not understand the "ins
and outs of how things are going to be implemented at the unit level."
But nurses do. They can be the "reality check" she says boards need.
It is a misconception, says Hassmiller, that "if you have a physician
representative either on a board or providing testimony on Capitol Hill,
or whatever, that he or she is a representative of the entire healthcare
workforce." This, she stresses, is not the case. And that is exactly the role
that nurses are poised to fill.

Linda Procci, who recently retired after 17 years as VP of Service Line
Operations at Cedars-Sinai Medical Center in Los Angeles, agrees.
"Having a good balance of men and women on a board is important,"
says Procci. "But having more nurses is also important because part of
our training was focused not only on caring about the individual patient
in front of us, but also caring deeply about the impact on community or
public health."

Therese Fitzpatrick is a principal with Healthcare Transformation Services-Philips Healthcare in Chicago. She serves on several boards of directors, including the editorial board of the journal *Nursing Economic$*; Advocate Good Samaritan Hospital, Illinois; Turning Point Community Mental Health Center, Illinois; and the advisory board for the College of Science and Health at DePaul University, Chicago.

Board service, says Fitzpatrick, was a natural progression of her career and the various leadership roles she held. "My interest has always been how to make healthcare organizations fit into the bigger social and urban network," she says. "If you want to change things, you have to leave that staffer's position and get into a manager role, or into the C-suite. Then, if you *really* want to change the bigger system, you have to be able to influence at that board governance level."

She points to her own experience as a member of the President's Council for Advocate. "I am the only nurse who chairs one of the Advocate organizations," she says. "They will look to me for a nursing perspective on issues—I cannot think of a meeting that goes by where that has not happened." This is true, she says, even though there are physicians among the members of the group.

Joanne Disch is professor ad honorem at the University of Minnesota School of Nursing. She has served as a chief nurse executive in two major medical centers, acted as interim dean at the University of Minnesota School of Nursing, and held numerous national leadership positions, such as president of the American Association of Critical-Care Nurses, chair of the American Nurses Association (ANA) Committee on Nursing Practice and Standards, and board member and chair of the national board of American Association of Retired Persons (AARP). Currently, she is a member of the board of Aurora Health Care and chair of the board of Chamberlain College of Nursing. She is the immediate past president of the American Academy of Nursing.

Her first board experience was with the American Association of Critical-Care Nurses. Joanne was influenced to get involved by a mentor from graduate school. "She was on the board, and they needed somebody to be on a committee, so I went out to California with her, got to meet some of the people and could really see the potential. I thought, 'This is really pretty interesting stuff.'"

"Nurses," she says, "bring a lot to the boardroom and have a bold plan—they have the big picture, they understand context, and they're very skilled communicators. They are good at picking up both verbal and nonverbal cues, and they're disproportionately skilled in telling a story that is going to resonate with somebody, no matter who it is."

Susan Groenwald, president of Chamberlain College of Nursing, adds that, "People are selected for boards for a variety of reasons, including their personal skills and attributes. A nurse may bring skills that others don't have. Nurses are known for hard work, the ability to problem solve, and for collaboration. But others may have those skills as well—and not all nurses have them."

Still, it would be difficult for anyone to argue that nurses would not be able to provide highly valued insights for healthcare organizations through board membership. Yet, there is an abundance of data indicating that nurses are woefully underrepresented on hospital and healthcare boards.

A 2004–2005 study of governance in matched groups of high-performing versus mid-range performing community hospitals (Prybil, et al., 2012) found that only 2% of voting board members in both groups were nurses actively engaged in practice in these or other healthcare institutions. By comparison, 26% of their board members were physicians.

A 2008–2009 study of governance structures and practices in 123 non-profit community health systems (Prybil, et al., 2008)—all of which were operating two or more hospitals and other health programs in a single community—found that 2.4% of voting board members were nurses, while 22% were physicians. Similarly, a study of governance in 14 of the nation's 15 largest nonprofit health systems completed in 2012 (Prybil et al, 2012) also found that on an overall basis, 6% of the systems' voting board members were nurses. However, the proportion is not uniform among the systems. Nine of the 14 systems are faith-based (eight sponsored or controlled by Roman Catholic entities, one Adventist-sponsored). In combination, 9% of the voting members of the faith-based system boards were nurses; among the five secular systems, only 2% of voting board members were nurses.

The situation is not much better for women as a whole.

WOMEN IN GOVERNANCE ROLES

In the United States, only 19.2% of corporate board seats are held by women, according to research by Catalyst (2014), an organization dedicated to expanding opportunities for women in business. The situation for women in board chair roles is even more grim. According to Catalyst, in the United States, only 3.2% of board chairs are female.

And, despite some progress made over the past several decades, the "good old boy club" sadly still exists, indicates Jacquelyn Campbell, professor and Anna D. Wolf Chair at Johns Hopkins School of Nursing and national program director of the Robert Wood Johnson Foundation nurse faculty scholars. One of her board experiences made that abundantly clear. "It's been fascinating because I have recently gained a little more direct understanding of a board culture dominated by men of a specific age group. They have a strong and consistent ability to lock arms and hold the line around their consistent way of operating. This may be a pattern that these men are unaware of. It is a posture that can eliminate creative and diverse thinking at the very time when new mental models in healthcare are so necessary."

Says Campbell, "This experience has made me think about how important it is for nurses to be in the places where impactful strategic healthcare decisions are made because old models of thinking will not take us successfully into a new future. I hate to sound so critical, but we must have input from decision-makers who actually reflect the broad and diverse populations that healthcare serves rather than having decisions made only by the privileged minority. The biggest challenge in changing the composition of our boards lies in the fact that those who are privileged rarely see themselves that way."

Laurie Benson, CEO of LSB Unlimited, has served on seven corporate boards in the technology, finance, insurance, manufacturing, and services industries, and has been actively engaged in the healthcare industry through board service and executive leadership roles. She currently serves on five private company boards and five nonprofit boards.

"My very first board experience was with independent living where we got the first HUD-approved senior housing in Wisconsin, I'm proud to say," says Benson. "My first corporate board was the largest independent insurance company in Wisconsin." She served on that board for 10 years, at which time she recommended that the new CEO refresh the board. In addition, Benson created her own board of directors for her technology company. "So, in addition to my board service, I was the beneficiary of a wonderful board of directors in my technology company. I credit them in large part for the success and sustainability of my company."

Campbell and Benson are, unfortunately, in the minority. And, in fact, the United States lags behind Europe and a lot of the rest of the world in terms of female representation on boards. The country with the most board seats held by women (at 40.5%) is Norway, according to Catalyst (2014), followed by Sweden (27%), Finland (26.8%), the United Kingdom (20.7%), and France (18.3%). The United States is at 16.9%.

You need only to look at the board make-up of your local hospital, or the hospital where you work, to see that this situation is very real. It is a situation, though, that represents opportunities for nurses.

When I joined the DeVry Education Group board, a woman was chair of the nominating committee. I am certain that she stressed the importance of recruiting another woman. Prior to her recent retirement we had three women—approximately 30% of the board! I am convinced that it was the DeVry board's experience with women board members that gave them the confidence and courage to elect me to serve as chair of their board.

Unfortunately, women board chairs remain woefully low. The MSCI 2014 Survey of Women on Boards reports the world average of female chairs in industrialized sectors at 4% and emerging markets at 3%.

Other countries are helping women make significant inroads to board service, and this shift is largely due to establishing requirements for organizations to recruit women to their boards. France, for instance, has a law requiring companies on the stock exchange that make at least $50 million in euros with 500 or more employees must have women representing at least 40% of its board make-up by 2017 (Biggs, A., 2014). Norway was the first nation to establish quotas for women board members, effective 2008 (*Economist,* 2014). "Since then gender quotas for boards have been imposed in Belgium, Iceland, Italy, the Netherlands and Spain (though with less severe sanctions: non-complying firms must generally explain in their annual reports why they fell short and what they plan to do about it). The European Commission is considering imposing quotas across the EU. Malaysia has imposed a 30% quota for new appointments to boards, and Brazil a 40% target, though only for state-controlled firms" (*Economist*, 2014).

The MSCI 2014 Survey of Women on Boards report shows an interesting phenomenon that suggests a direct correlation between an increase in women on boards (WOB) and a decreased incidence of governance-related controversies:

> We found that companies with a higher percentage of WOB tend to have fewer governance-related controversies, including fraud, accounting, bribery, and corruption-related controversies, in the last three years. Further, companies with higher percentages of women on boards had higher ESG risk management ratings and strategies across virtually all risk issues (MSCI, 2014, p. 2).

In the United States, the 2020 Women on Boards organization has launched a national campaign to see women's representation on boards rise to 20% by 2020.

Shareholders and consumers can be effective in pressuring corporations to put women and minorities on their boards. 2020 Women on Boards is active in educating the public, committed to its cause, and gives recognition to organizations that have at least 20% of women on their boards.

Sign up at www.2020wob.com to support the effort to increase the number of women on boards and receive updates about the corporations that do—and don't—have female representation on their boards.

MINORITIES IN GOVERNANCE ROLES

In 2014, the Institute for Diversity in Health Management of the AHA released findings from its biannual survey, "Diversity and Disparities: A Benchmarking Study of U.S. Hospitals." Although the survey indicated some progress being made, the institute's president and CEO Fred Hobby said in a news release, "We know we have more work to do and are committed to finding new avenues to promote diversity within the healthcare field."

The release further noted, "As a demographic trend, the patient population represented by minorities has grown by 2 percent and was found to be 31 percent in 2013. However, minority representation in hospital leadership and governance lagged with only 14 percent of hospital board members and an average of 12 percent of executive leadership positions comprising minorities."

Campbell: "I'm one of the few women on a board I sit on now, and I am the only nurse on that board, and the dominance of the white male mental model is stunning."

REFERENCES

American Hospital Association Center for Healthcare Governance. (2007). *2007 blue ribbon panel report: Building an exceptional board: Effective practices for health care governance.* Author. http://www.americangovernance.com/resources/reports/brp/2007/

American Hospital Association Institute for Diversity in Health Management (June 1, 2014). Diversity and disparities: A benchmarking study of U.S. hospitals. http://www.hpoe.org/resources/hpoehretaha-guides/803

Biggs, A. (27 August 2014). Gender balance on French corporate boards of directors. http://www.leadingboards.com/en/blog/gender-balance-on-french-corporate-boards-of-directors/

Catalyst. (2014). 2014 Catalyst census: Women Board Directors. Author. http://www.catalyst.org/system/files/2014_catalyst_census_women_board_directors_0.pdf

Gamble, M (2014). 10 challenges and opportunities for hospitals in 2014. *Becker's Hospital Review*, 2014(1), 1, 8-10.

MSCI. (2014). Executive Summary: 2014 Survey of Women on Boards. Author. https://www.msci.com/resources/research/articles/2014/Executive_Summary-2014_Survey_of_Women_on_Boards.pdf

Prybil, L., Levey, S., Killian, R., Fardo, D., Chait, R., Bardach, D. R., & Roach, W. (2012). Governance in large nonprofit health systems: Current profile and emerging patterns in health management and policy faculty book gallery. University of Kentucky UKnowledge. Lexington: KY.

Prybil, L., Levey, S., Peterson, R., Heinrich, D., Brezinski, P, Price, J., ... Roach, W. (2008). Governance in nonprofit community health systems: An initial report on CEO perspectives. Grant Thornton, LLP. Chicago, IL. file:///C:/Users/carla/Downloads/2008-prybil-report.pdf

3

WHAT NURSES NEED TO KNOW TO GET ON BOARD(S)

For many nurses, governance is an unknown. Few nurses, as earlier chapters explored, have experience in governance, and many do not understand what the role of the board is as it interacts with an organization's chief executive officer (CEO) and senior staff. In this chapter, I offer you the inside scoop about board governance.

GOVERNING VERSUS DOING

Boards operate at the highest levels of governance—or they should! As those who have served on boards will tell you, there is a wide range of difference between boards and their focus. At the corporate level, you are most likely to see boards governing at a high strategic level, focused on strategic direction, profits, and the health of the company. In smaller, nonprofit boards (and in hospital and nursing association boards), it is not uncommon to find the focus on more operational, less strategic issues such as budgets, human resources, and other day-to-day business activities. This is something that I believe needs to change. Governance is about *governing*, it is not about *doing*. Doing is the work of the management team for the organization you serve. Gladys Campbell, CEO of the Northwest Organization of Nurse Executives and chief nurse executive and senior leader for clinical strategy for the Washington State Hospital Association, believes that lesson can be hard to learn, especially because most nurses begin their board experience through small local boards.

> When you're on a board for a small organization that has no staff, you begin your board experience believing that your job as a board member is to do operational work. An early experience like this is hard to shake and prevents some from having an easy shift to a strategic leadership role as a board member.

Campbell also served on some advisory boards that gave her a skewed perspective of "real" board service. "Advisory boards can create confusion," she says. "You think you're having a board experience, and you're really not because the role of an advisory board is not governance." (See Chapter 1, "Board Basics," for more exploration of advisory boards.)

It was not until the late 1990s, when Campbell assumed a board role with the American Association of Critical-Care Nurses at the national level, that she says, "The light bulb went on, and it became crystal clear that my board role was not about operations. It was about being a strategic leader!"

Therese Fitzpatrick, the principal clinical strategic consultant for Healthcare Transformation Services within Philips Healthcare, agrees that it's important for nurses to understand the critical distinction between governance and management. "They are two very different sets of leadership skills," she says. "One is, certainly, more about doing; the other is around influencing and advising. As nurses, we tend to get into a 'Let's roll up the sleeves and get in there and do it ourselves,'" she notes. "You simply can't do that at the governance level. That's often really hard for nurses to understand."

BOARDS OPERATE AS A UNIT

Nurses often are singularly focused on their nursing perspective and background when they are called to serve.

Laurie Benson, a veteran board director, corporate executive, and entrepreneur, notes that boards operate as a unit, which is another concept that can initially be difficult to grasp. "The board's success is measured by their collective contribution, not that of any individual board member," she says.

"You need to bring the nursing perspective," says Susan Hassmiller, senior adviser for nursing for the Robert Wood Johnson Foundation. "You need a larger view of the world outside of nursing. You need to connect the dots." Too often, she says, she hears concerns about the role that nurses play on the few boards they are involved with. "One of the things I hear is that nurses just want to talk about nursing," she says.

Daniel Pesut, a professor and experienced board leader, says that it is crucial for board members to be able to "think at different levels of perspective," something that needs to be fully appreciated.

"All of the time you're thinking about what's going on in the meta, macro, and micro environment," he says. "You need to be able to transcend and include all of those different perspectives to identify and intervene when a discussion in a board is occurring at an inappropriate logical level."

BOARD MEMBER ACQUISITION PROCESS

The recruitment process for boards varies among nonprofits; for-profits; start-ups; and, often, companies. There are commonalities, though. Understanding the process can help.

Traditional board member recruitment and selection processes seek board members with backgrounds that match the organization's strategic priorities. Each potential new board member is rated on the skills and attributes that the board needs in order to address the organization's mission and strategic priorities.

CURRENT NEEDS

The Georgia Center for Nonprofits (GCN) developed three chart templates that should assist directors in identifying strategic needs, inventorying priority skill sets, and recruiting attributes for future board members.

The current board members are analyzed in terms of the new skill sets; if the current board possesses all the skills needed to achieve the organization's strategic goals, there may be no need to search for new board members. However, if there are needed skills that none of the current board members possess, there should be a search process for new board members. Table 3.1 shows an example of one organization's strategic needs. Figure 3.1 is the GCN's template.

ORGANIZATION'S STRATEGIC NEEDS

The strategic needs table (see Table 3.1 and Figure 3.1) indicates that this hospital has four strategic goals: to ensure financial viability under the new healthcare payment policies, implement an EHR across the system, create partnerships with select clinicians and other organizations, and create patient- and family-focused care across the continuum.

After recording the organization's strategic needs, the board and management identify the *essential skills* that would address their goals. The essential skills vary from information technology (IT), to mergers and acquisitions, to discharge planning and patient education.

TABLE 3.1 STRATEGIC NEEDS TABLE EXAMPLE

Goal 1	Goal 2	Goal 3	Goal 4
Ensure financial viability in the new pay-for-performance environment	Implement the appropriate electronic health record (EHR)	Create partnerships with the right physicians, clinics, and other healthcare organizations	Improve quality metrics relative to readmission rates and patient-/family-centered care
Payor	IT	Contracting	Discharge planning
Contracting	Training/education	M&A	Ambulatory care
Bundling	Clinical practice	Ambulatory care	Patient education

Use this **Strategic Needs Table** to list strategic goals and the skill sets needed to execute the strategies involved.

Strategic Needs Table				
GOAL 1 (e.g., Open new facility)	GOAL 2	GOAL 3	GOAL 4	GOAL 5
Skill set 1 (e.g., Commercial construction)				

Provided by the Georgia Center for Nonprofits (Beaver, 2014)

Figure 3.1 Strategic Needs Table Template

CURRENT SKILLS

After assessing board needs, but before searching for new members, the current board inventory (see Table 3.2 and Figure 3.2) is completed. It describes the skills of the current board members. When looking at this organization's board members and their skills, it is clear that they have adequate skills in contracting, legal, and finance. There appear to be no current board members who are skillful in discharge planning, patient education, and clinical education.

Another approach to completing this current board inventory is to conduct a brief survey of the board members. Ask the board members to rate their skills on each of the essential skills you have identified. They can rate themselves on a 1-5 scale, indicating that they are an expert (5) or a novice (1).

Interviewing members often yields skills that others may not be aware of, helping reveal what skills are needed in new board members.

TABLE 3.2   CURRENT BOARD INVENTORY EXAMPLE

	Contracting	Legal	Finance	Discharge Planning	Patient Education	Clinical Education
Ms. Jones	X					
Mr. Smith			X			
Mr. Brown	X					
Mr. White			X			
Ms. Nightingale		X				

Use this **Current Board Inventory** template to list current board members in the left-hand column and the skill sets needed from the Strategic Needs Table across the top.

Current Board Inventory				
PRIORITY SKILL SETS	SKILL SET 1	SKILL SET 2	SKILL SET 3	SKILL SET 4
Board Member A				

Provided by the Georgia Center for Nonprofits (Beaver, 2014)

Figure 3.2 Current Board Inventory Template

RECRUIT SKILLS

The recruit attributes chart provides an approach to comparing and contrasting the skills and attributes of potential board members. A picture will emerge of the gaps in critical skills based on the organization's strategy and goals, the board's assessment of the professional skills of current members, and individual board members' self-assessments.

These gaps serve as the basis for evaluation to be used in searching and recruiting potential board candidates. After these needs are identified, board members will often consider who, among their network of contacts, might have the skills needed and then approach these individuals for potential board membership. Candidates are then evaluated based on the desired attributes that have been identified and are shown in Table 3.3 and Figure 3.3.

TABLE 3.3 RECRUIT ATTRIBUTES CHART EXAMPLE

Candidate	Available Time	Racial Diversity	Geographic Diversity	Contacts with Potential Donors	Assertive/ Positive	Aligned with Needed Skills/ Mission
A. North, Advance Practice Nurse	X				X	X
B. South, CPA	X	X		X		X
C. East, College Professor	X		X	X		
D. West, Retired CEO	X			X		X

Use this **Recruit Attributes Chart** template to list recruitment possibilities in the left-hand column and desired attributes across the top row. (Desired attributes can be changed and/or added to.)

Recruit Attributes Chart						
CANDIDATES	HAS TIME	RACIAL DIVERSITY	GEO-GRAPHIC REACH	ACCESS TO DONORS	ASSERTIVE/ POSITIVE	ATTACHMENT TO MISSION
(Skill: Banking)						
Candidate A						
Candidate B						

Provided by the Georgia Center for Nonprofits (Beaver, 2014)

Figure 3.3   Recruit Attributes Chart Template

Laurie Benson notes that most of her board experiences were driven by referrals. "While I didn't necessarily know the leadership, I was referred to them," she says.

Boards often use a matrix or profile of needed skills and expertise to understand their current composition and then seek new members to fill gaps. Competency-based selection adds a behavioral dimension and seeks trustees with the knowledge, skills, and personal behaviors that can lead to a high-performing board and organization.

Today it is becoming increasingly likely that boards will be seeking "out-of-community" trustees. It's a topic that James Gauss covered in an article for the Center for Healthcare Governance: "Recruiting the Right Mix" (Gauss, Valentine, 2013). In it, he and coauthor Steven T. Valentine provide both pros and cons of casting a wider net.

The pros include the ability to:

- Enhance existing skill sets, knowledge base, and talents
- Bring new ideas and perspectives to the board and executive leadership
- Deal with difficult or sensitive situations in fresh, innovative ways
- Add strong professional and personal reputations to attract additional talent over time
- Bring on greater fundraising capability

There are drawbacks, however. Those potential members may:

- Lack specific experience with the communities served
- Lack local contacts

- Struggle with the time commitment and geographic location

- Micromanage or forget to focus on the board

Each board will have to grapple with these issues and make decisions based on their own unique position in the community; the stakeholders they serve; and their mission, vision, and strategic priorities.

Using a competency-based approach to selecting board members requires new tools and practices. Competency-focused interview tools, for example, focus on how candidates have used needed competencies in other settings and how they might apply them to issues facing the hospital. These tools enable boards not only to identify people with needed backgrounds and skills, but also to distinguish, from among several good candidates, the one that best meets the board's needs.

As you are being considered for a board position, it is highly likely that you will go through an interview process similar to the one used in traditional job recruitment.

What kinds of questions might you be asked?

- When were you involved in leading a group or organization through significant change? Briefly describe the change and how you provided leadership in moving change initiatives forward.

- How did you maintain a focus on strategies and values during the change?

- How did you guide the group or organization to stay the course throughout the change process?

- How did you help overcome obstacles or resistance to change?

The interview process is a great opportunity for board members and the potential new board member to learn more about each other.

- After the change process was completed, how did you help the group or organization envision the next wave of change?

ORIENTATION

Boards are only as strong as their weakest member, and effective boards understand that good governance begins with the individual board member. Even those who have served on other boards, or who have extensive board experience, need to learn about this new organization they will be governing and the environment in which it operates.

Nonprofit organizations are among the most complex of organizations. So to be effective individually, and as part of the team, new board members need an orientation, ideally prior to coming onto the board or within the first few months of joining.

Orientation to board service should be a structured process rather than a one-time event—and, in the case of a hospital or healthcare organization, should review the healthcare environment, both national and local, including the hospital's competitors. Boards in other industries should do the same sort of orientation. Orientation should also cover information about the organization's structure, including programs, services, and senior executives, as well as its key stakeholders and their needs and expectations. New board members also need to understand the organization's strategic framework, which includes its vision, mission, values, goals, and strategies.

A discussion of key organizational partners is important. Hospital board members, for instance, should be educated about the organization's relationship with the medical staff and with other groups and organizations that are the hospital's strategic partners. In the case of universities, issues related to the faculty, alumni, and the board are key relationships that need to be described and discussed.

Board orientation should clarify the board's roles; responsibilities; structure, including board leaders and committees; and governance infrastructure, such as policies, procedures, key board practices, supporting staff, meetings, and other expectations and requirements that are often detailed in board and board member job descriptions. Orientation should also clarify board culture to help new members understand how the board works together and with key organizational leaders.

Finally, new board members need information about individual responsibilities regarding issues such as conflict of interest and confidentiality. Furthermore, new board members should review the organization's directors and officer's liability insurance policy and what it covers. Best practices include having the organization's general counsel provide an orientation session on the board members' legal and ethical responsibilities.

Effective orientation processes also include:

- Time with board leaders, the CEO, and other senior leaders—for instance, the chief nurse in a hospital setting

- A tour of the organization and all its facilities

- Supporting materials, such as an orientation handbook and board policies and procedures manual

- Information about other educational resources available to the board and how to take advantage of them

A seasoned board member who serves as a mentor for the first year of service can help a new board member get up to speed more quickly by answering questions and clarifying board practices and culture. It is common to encourage new board members to participate in an education process that provides knowledge related to trustee core competencies.

BOARD EDUCATION AND DEVELOPMENT

Board education should focus on improving knowledge and skills of the board and on overall board performance.

Many boards ensure that at least some of their education sessions involve board members, executives, and clinical leaders in learning together and discussing applications to the organization. This frequently happens at board and leadership retreats.

A comprehensive board development program also includes succession plans for board leaders, including board officers and committee chairs. Succession should build leadership continuity and provide opportunities for candidates to acquire or further develop needed competencies. Performance evaluation for the full board, individual members, and board leaders is an important step in fostering continuous governance improvement and is discussed later in this chapter.

Because people learn best in different ways, board education should use a variety of methods, including board meeting education sessions; off-site programs; online, written, and other approaches tailored to adult learning needs.

Assessments are often done via survey, interview, and discussion among stakeholder representatives, the board, and hospital leadership.

A stakeholder assessment is a good opportunity to hear directly from stakeholders about their needs and expectations.

After stakeholder feedback is gathered and analyzed, the board and leaders prioritize stakeholder needs and expectations. Establishing priorities is necessary to provide a clear framework for board and organizational decision-making.

BOARD/CEO INTERACTION

The difference between the roles of governance and management has long been a topic of debate. Some have the impression that a solid immutable line exists between these roles that should never be crossed. However, nothing could be further from the truth or from actual practice.

Boards and management will define their roles and responsibilities differently, depending on situations or characteristics that are unique to different organizations. The common practice is that the board provides oversight and the management team executes organizational operations, but this can vary depending on the situation. One example of this occurs when organizations are in crisis. In a hospital that is in need of a performance turnaround or that has experienced an abrupt departure of its CEO, the board may appropriately step in to oversee daily operations until the organization is back on track.

Boards and executives may also define their roles and responsibilities differently across different areas, depending on each party's level of expertise and understanding. Boards with members who have strong backgrounds in quality and patient safety, for example, may take a larger role in overseeing this area than they would in other areas where the board may have less expertise. It is also likely that the relative roles of the board and management may shift over time as board composition changes, the needs of the organization change, or the CEO leaves or retires.

Some level of difference among board and CEO roles in organizations is therefore appropriate. However, these roles should be explicitly determined and periodically reviewed by each board/CEO team to achieve the necessary balance. Boards must govern—not manage. Management is the CEO's job.

HEALTHCARE TRENDS

Making sure that relative roles are clear and agreed upon is becoming more important as market and regulatory forces are compelling boards to govern at levels of detail that once would have been considered micromanagement, but are now required and necessary in the current environment of heightened governance accountability.

One important point to make is that the CEO is typically the *only* member of the organization that reports to the board. All other staff members report up through the organization to the CEO. That relationship is depicted in Figure 3.4.

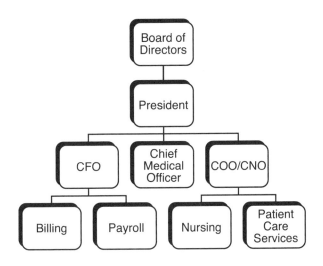

Figure 3.4 Organizational Chart

However, as the board's direct report, the CEO also has the responsibility to help the board do its job well. The CEO is responsible for leading the organization and managing the executive team while executing the board policies and decisions. When it comes to working with the board, the CEO is responsible for identifying issues requiring board focus; putting them into context; and providing the board with information, recommendations, and alternative courses of action to make good decisions. Boards should have the expectation that their CEOs will provide them with the information that they need well enough in advance of board meetings to allow for thoughtful preparation.

Most relationships function best when both parties keep each other informed of important issues and potential concerns. The board/CEO relationship is no exception.

Of course, a successful board/CEO partnership is a two-way street. This means that boards should meet expectations that CEOs have as well. Expectations that CEOs should have of their boards include:

- Coming to meetings prepared and ready to raise questions and discuss issues

- Acting at all times in the best interests of the organization's stakeholders

- Drawing key issues to the CEO's attention and discussing them with the CEO

- Maintaining an open, honest, collaborative relationship

- Setting clear performance goals and providing feedback in a meaningful and timely way

- Disclosing and dealing appropriately with all conflicts of interest

- Keeping board business confidential

- Allowing management to run the organization

- Preventing others from circumventing the CEO to get to the board

- Being committed to board and governance effectiveness

As previously mentioned, the CEO is typically the only executive who reports to the board. All other executives report to the CEO or chief operating officer (COO). Board members must remember that it is their role to communicate their concerns to the CEO and not the individual members of the executive team. The board enables the CEO to do his or her job, and the CEO enables the board to do its job.

SUCCESSION PLANNING

Routine succession planning ideally starts 2 to 3 years in advance to give most boards the time needed to conduct a careful, thorough process.

Succession planning increases the availability of experienced and capable people who are ready to assume new roles as they become available. A formalized succession planning process benefits employees. Candidates see the critical career paths and core competencies that the organization desires. They can then consider their own competencies and areas of opportunity for development and, in concert with their managers, find ways to develop needed skills. If an employee wants to become the VP of Human Resources some day, for instance, that employee can find out what is needed to move into this role and then work with his or her manager to identify

Succession planning is the process for identifying and developing internal people who have the potential to fill key business leadership positions, including the top position—the CEO.

gaps and critical learning experiences. This same process can be cascaded down through the organization as it considers its vice president, director, and management levels.

Hiring from within has three positive effects. First, internal succession has a positive impact on others in the organization. When your strong internal staff members see internal candidates being promoted, they feel confident that they might have these opportunities themselves. They are less likely, therefore, to seek positions with other organizations. Second, developing leadership from within results in savings realized from not having to invest in search firms, marketing, and advertising for open positions. Third, there is much literature to suggest that promoting internal candidates into leadership positions leads to a more successful outcome than hiring candidates from outside the organization. Internal candidates tend to be more successful, so boards are taking the succession of internal candidates more seriously.

Internal candidates succeed for a variety of reasons. Most notably, they understand the culture. They have built relationships and have a network within the organization. They come with a level of experience that external candidates simply can't match. They don't have to learn the business from the base: They already know it.

At one organization that I am familiar with, management bonuses are tied directly to staff development. Regardless of what area of the organization they manage, they are expected to develop their staff so that 20% of their staff, annually, moves into more responsible roles. So, individual bonuses are directly tied to talent development. That sends a strong message—and it drives results.

Another organization that I work with requires that the chief human resource officer make an annual presentation to the board on the succession planning process and program. Essentially, this consists of what you see in Figure 3.5: a set of charts that show the current CEO, with that person's picture, three or four other photos under that with a list of strengths, and a list of development opportunities. Year to year, these photos change as successors are developed and moved into roles that become open. The process provides an opportunity to be proactive in terms of identifying the strengths that will be needed—and the individuals within the organization who have those strengths or who could develop them.

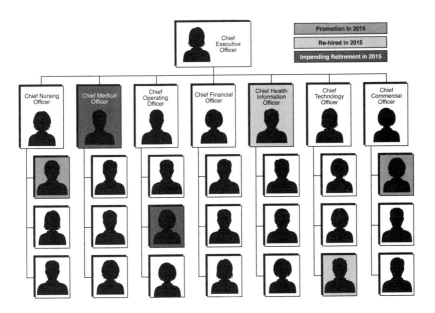

Figure 3.5   Senior Leadership Team Changes

As these individuals are identified, they are targeted for development.

Some people continue on the list as high potentials, while others drop off because they are no longer progressing toward a particular role. Individual assessments allow the organization to evaluate this potential over time. Some will rise in the list, and some will come off the list over time.

Development might involve attaining an advanced degree, getting experience in some other aspect of the business, or perhaps getting global experience.

An annual review is a nice way of gaining a visual sense of the talent bench—who is on the bench, how diverse the bench is, and where they are moving on and off the bench. This annual review also provides some insight into the managers within the organization. Some are skilled in getting their staff members the kind of critical developmental experiences they need, but others are not. That tells you something. Those managers who are not able to effectively develop high-potential staff may have hit their career ceiling themselves.

A form like the one in Figure 3.6 provides a tangible way of conducting and tracking this analysis.

If something happens to the CEO, and no succession plan is in place, the board—and you—will be held accountable. Succession planning for the CEO position is a very important board responsibility.

Unfortunately, in many cases, the CEO does not readily welcome board discussions about his or her own successors. Even though these interactions can be sensitive, they are necessary.

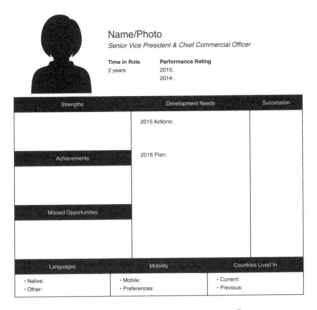

Figure 3.6   Individual Assessment Form

EMERGENCY CEO SUCCESSION

In addition to a well-organized succession planning process, boards will often have an emergency succession plan at the CEO level of the organization in the event of some unforeseen incident—say, the CEO is hit by a beer truck or wins the lottery. Such things have happened!

Thus, take time to consider, in the event of such a crisis, what the board would do.

- Who would immediately move into that role as an interim CEO to help get through the crisis?
- What information would be released to the community and external environment through a news release?
- Who else would need to be contacted?
- How would these contacts take place?

Boards should always have CEO succession on their agenda. The CEO should be involved in emergency succession planning, which should take place at least once yearly. The board, or a committee of the board, should sit down with the CEO and the head of HR to have the emergency succession discussion.

Sometimes the discussion is straightforward and clear cut; in other cases, it may not be. Perhaps the CEO feels that Christine should be the successor, but the board feels that Kelly would be a better choice. This is an opportunity not only for resolution, but also for learning. The board could learn what it is that the CEO sees in Christine that makes him feel that she would be the best choice to inherit the position. The board could then share with the CEO why it feels that Kelly would be the better choice: What skills/competencies does Kelly have that the board feels are important for future growth and success?

MISCONCEPTIONS

Because the CEO succession process is complicated, boards may hold some erroneous thoughts.

Save money. Boards should take on parts of the process to save costs. CEO succession usually requires the assistance of a professional search firm.

Find a similar replacement. A second error is assuming the new CEO should be like the existing one. This assumption is based on the belief that the future will look like the past—which is almost never true. Many boards are more comfortable with and favor candidates that have been CEOs in the past. Looking only at people with prior CEO experience will cause some boards to overlook candidates who have reported directly to a CEO and who have characteristics and experience suited to taking the next step. Delegating the entire succession process should go to the existing CEO or to outside professionals. That is an abdication of the board's responsibility. When a CEO fails, one of the most important steps for the board is to look in the mirror and commit to the rigorous due diligence needed to avoid future mistakes.

Plans, Goldsmith suggests, do not develop anyone—only developmental experiences develop people. Further, he suggests, organizations (and, by default, boards) should measure the outcomes of these efforts rather than the process itself. These metrics might include things such as the percentage of executive level vacancies that have been filled with internal candidates compared with external hires; the percentage of promotions that have come from the pool of high-potential internal candidates; and employee turnover, at all levels of the organization.

In a 2009 article in *Harvard Business Review,* Marshall Goldsmith suggested that the name of the process be changed from *succession planning* to *succession development* (2009).

Nurse managers and executives have valuable experience in the areas of employee recruitment and retention, which are great board assets.

CEO EVALUATION AND COMPENSATION

As a board member, you will evaluate the organization's or corporation's CEO. Therese Fitzpatrick says nurses, "need to understand what that role is about and how to set expectations with other executives. That was always an eye-opening experience for me—realizing that I was in a position where I potentially had to coach and counsel and provide performance feedback to an executive. I think that CEO evaluation and CEO executive planning, succession planning are real shockers," she says. "You just don't think that that's part of your job and what a big part of the job it is."

HEALTHCARE TRENDS

CEO evaluation and compensation remain a focus of the healthcare media. The August 11, 2014 cover of *Modern Healthcare* has the headline "CEO Pay Still Soaring" (Landen). The article states that the average 2012 cash compensation for CEOs was $2.2 million. *Modern Healthcare* states that the average CEO received a 7.4% increase between 2011 and 2012, while the average hospital employee received a 2% salary increase. Board members are responsible for CEO compensation and are the focus of inquiry and criticism for excessive salaries. Compensation consultants can provide the data and expertise that board members need to make sound compensation decisions.

EVALUATION

Effective CEO evaluation processes share several common characteristics:

- **Collaborative:** The board and CEO work together and view performance management as an ongoing process rather than a one-time event. This view supports a mutual commitment to "no surprises" and enables the board to provide feedback as needed, rather than waiting until the annual evaluation, when it's too late for the CEO to address board concerns.

- **Formal:** This means following steps that are explicit and routinely followed.

- **Goal- and outcome-based:** Expectations and goals also provide a trigger for both parties to raise and discuss unforeseen issues that could have an impact on performance outcomes.

- **Conducted regularly:** Boards and CEOs that work together each year to set clear expectations and goals have a touchstone for periodic performance check-ins as well as the year-end assessment.

The board's responsibilities in CEO performance management and compensation include:

- **Setting performance goals and expectations**

  Although most CEOs are self-motivated and would need to be to rise to the position, the board needs to make sure the CEO knows what the board's expectations are and what the board cares most about. Providing ongoing feedback can help ensure that everyone is aligned.

- **Coaching and motivating the CEO**

- **Monitoring and evaluating performance**

- **Establishing compensation**

  This is done in conjunction with the board's Compensation committee, establishing the CEO's compensation. Bonuses are becoming a more common part of executive compensation. In the corporate world, executives receive a salary, an opportunity of an annual bonus, and long-term compensation incentives. Bonuses are an effective way of incenting executives toward goal achievement.

Performance management is most successful when it is a key aspect of the board/CEO relationship.

COMPENSATION AND BONUS

Compensation programs are a key board responsibility and usually require the assistance of a compensation consultant.

When the board and executive team have clearly defined operational goals, these goals become the basis of the bonus program. In the corporate world, the opportunity to earn bonuses for extraordinary performance is routine. Depending on the level of the employee, the bonus may be cash or cash and stock.

HEALTHCARE TRENDS

More nonprofit organizations are incorporating bonuses into their compensation strategy. In one of the hospitals where I was a board member, the executive team had the opportunity to increase compensation by 30% annually through a bonus system. The bonuses were tied to achieving very specific goals at a very specific level. If patient satisfaction increased by 3%, the executives might get a 10% bonus but would receive a 25% bonus for a 10% increase in patient satisfaction.

Most healthcare organizations have goals related to patient outcomes, patient satisfaction, and financial performance. Superb performance is dependent on all of the employees understanding these goals and working toward their achievement. Healthcare delivery is a team activity, and when the entire team is aligned, there is rapid progress on goal attainment. When I was on the board of Silver Cross Hospital, all of the employees were engaged in the organization's focus on achieving Solucient Top 100 status (http://100tophospitals.com/). When that goal was achieved, all of the employees were given bonuses and rewarded with a celebration.

BOARD DEVELOPMENT AND EVALUATION

Over the years, the concept of board evaluation has expanded beyond the full board to include board leaders, committees, and members. The board's Governance committee usually oversees the process.

Board evaluation is a process of self-assessment.

Healthcare organization boards have conducted board evaluations for more than 20 years. Spurred by The Joint Commission (TJC) standard requiring boards to evaluate their own performance, the process allows boards to look back and plan ahead, thus fostering the evaluation of strengths, weaknesses, and accomplishments while promoting action planning for continuous performance improvement.

Jim Gauss, of Witt/Kieffer, provides some perspective on the attributes of each of these types of boards. His insights are summarized in Table 3.4.

TABLE 3.4 CHARACTERISTICS OF HIGH-PERFORMING BOARDS*

High-performing boards	• An engaged and educated board chair • Careful succession planning • Clarity around mission and key organization strategies • Strong partnership with the CEO • Proactive about recruitment • Best practices utilization • Willing to challenge the status quo
Mid-range–performing boards	• Recognition of the importance of governance • CEO allowance to do his/her job • Striving to become better through best practice governance
Poorly performing boards	• Weak leadership • Lack of focus on the future • Limited time on strategy • Haphazard board member recruitment • Generally stuck in the past

*Courtesy Jim Gauss

Ongoing evaluation of the board as a whole, as well as of individual board members, committees, and processes, can help boards become high performing and minimize the risk of losing their high performance over time.

INDIVIDUAL BOARD MEMBER EVALUATION

Individual board members should receive feedback on their performance. This process should be conducted, at a minimum, once every 2 years. This is typically done through a several-step process that includes:

- Confidential written member questionnaire
- Aggregate results tabulated and reported
- Board meeting in a retreat to discuss results
- Identification of performance strengths and weaknesses
- Development of a performance improvement action plan
- Regular monitoring of plan progress

The questionnaire identifies individual development needs and reaffirms the members' further commitment to board service. The questionnaire that is initially completed by board members should focus on how well the members understand and perform their key roles and responsibilities. The assessment of individual board member performance is designed to evaluate each trustee's knowledge of board roles and responsibilities and expectations of board members. Board member evaluations are usually based on assessing how well the individual complies with expectations and requirements that the board has established for its members.

Examples of these expectations can include attendance at board and committee meetings; participation in board discussion and debate; decision-making that reflects the organization's mission and vision; and adherence to board conflict-of-interest and confidentiality policies.

Most nonprofit boards that do conduct evaluations also look at the financial contributions of the board member. Nonprofit boards should assess individual board member performance as well, but many don't. In fact, there is only one nonprofit board that I have served on that had a quantitative approach to evaluating the contributions of board members.

Some nonprofit organizations specify how much the individual board members are expected to contribute annually, and this is taken into consideration during the evaluation process.

DePaul University uses what it calls a Trustee Engagement Report (Holtschneider, 2013) to assess board member performance on an annual basis. This metric-based approach to evaluation is based on a set of criteria initially developed by the DePaul University board of trustees. DePaul is the only nonprofit organization that I am aware of that has developed such a thorough and constructive approach to board evaluation. DePaul shared the information and its process to include in this book.

Three broad categories are assessed:

- **Philanthropy:** A weighted combination of giving over the course of a capital campaign with points for other activities during the academic year in support of the campaign. In 2010, the philanthropy score was weighted at 70% giving and 30% activity points.

- **Board participation:** An average of attendance percentage at board and committee meetings in the past academic year and points for committees served on, committees led, and committee meetings attending.

- **Other university involvement:** Points are given for participation in other university activities, such as serving on an advisory board, attending events, and other trustee activities outside meetings.

Under each of these broad categories, specific items are rated. Figure 3.7 shows what the final matrix looks like with the U.S. presidents' names used as placeholders.

Based on the individual scores and the frequency applied for each item, total scores are assigned in each category, and a final score is calculated. This chart shows the list of "board members" in order from highest to lowest score. Board members receive both a personal one-sheet overview of their performance as well as an indication of how they rank compared with the other board members. A mock individual evaluation sheet on Abraham Lincoln is shown in Figure 3.8.

This analysis is valuable to the board when considering reappointing board members; it may even result in people being dropped from the board if their performance is not deemed to be adequate. For board members, the assessment also indicates how they are doing relative to other board members and both areas of strength and opportunities for improvement.

Similar to a job description, such an assessment can provide you with a clear picture of performance expectations. The DePaul tool assists in strengthening the individual board members and the board as a whole.

Knowing about such an assessment before accepting a board position can also be helpful in terms of deciding whether you are willing to commit to the expectations the board will have of you.

NAME	PHILANTHROPY					BOARD AND COMMITTEE PARTICIPATION								UNIV. INVOLVEMENT		WEIGHTED TOTAL
	Cumulative Giving (2011-2015)	Frequency Score for Giving	Campaign Points for AY14-15	Frequency Score for Campaign Points	Total Campaign Engagement Score (1)	Attendance Percentage	Frequency Score for Attendance Percentage	# Committees Served in AY14-15	# Committees Chaired in AY14-15	# of Committee Meetings Attended in AY14-15	Total Committee Service Points	Frequency Score for Committee Service	Total Participation Engagement Score (2)	University Involvement Points	Frequency Score for University Involvement Points	Final Score (3)
Lincoln	900,000	8	8	9	8.30	88	8	6	4	29	39	10	9.00	22	10	8.82
Obama	1,250,000	9	3	4	7.50	90	9	2	1	3	6	8	8.50	11	7	7.95
Truman	2,400,000	9	7	8	8.70	85	7	3	0	5	8	9	8.00	2	3	7.78
Cleveland	800,000	8	8	9	8.30	75	5	3	0	4	7	8	6.50	13	8	7.37
Van Buren	4,000,000	10	8	9	9.70	87	8	1	0	3	4	3	5.50	11	7	7.33
Tyler	450,000	6	3	4	5.40	100	10	4	0	12	16	10	10.00	0	1	7.26
Taft	5,000,000	10	2	3	7.90	40	1	3	0	10	13	10	5.50	15	9	6.81
Grant	2,500,000	10	7	7	9.10	67	4	3	0	1	4	5	4.50	15	9	6.79
Harding	900,000	8	9	10	8.60	60	3	2	0	3	5	7	5.00	14	8	6.74
Monroe	715,000	7	8	8	7.30	100	10	1	0	3	4	3	6.50	16	5	6.67
Washington	3,800,000	10	4	5	8.50	83	7	1	0	2	3	2	4.50	5	9	6.55
Clinton	800,000	8	6	7	7.70	75	5	1	2	2	5	7	6.00	4	4	6.48
Harrison (W)	650,000	7	9	10	7.90	80	6	2	0	3	5	6	6.00	4	3	6.46
Reagan	90,000	4	3	2	3.40	90	9	3	1	4	8	9	9.00	4	4	6.26
Pierce	20,000	1	3	4	1.90	100	10	2	0	6	8	9	9.50	6	6	6.11
Roosevelt (T)	450,000	6	3	3	5.10	80	6	2	2	1	5	6	6.00	16	10	6.04

(1) Weighted at 70% of the Giving Frequency Score and 30% of Campaign Points Frequency Score

(2) Weighted 50% of Attendance Percentage Frequency Score and 50% of Committee Service Frequency Score

(3) Weighted at 40% of Philanthropy Engagement Score, 50% of Participation Engagement Score, and 10% of University Involvement Engagement Score

Figure 3.7 Board Member Evaluation Matrix

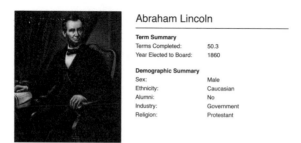

Abraham Lincoln

Term Summary
Terms Completed:	50.3
Year Elected to Board:	1860

Demographic Summary
Sex:	Male
Ethnicity:	Caucasian
Alumni:	No
Industry:	Government
Religion:	Protestant

Attendance Summary

Year	Committees	BOT
2013-2014	24 of 29 (82%)	3 of 3 (100%)
2012-2013	23 of 28 (82%)	3 of 3 (100%)
2011-2012	20 of 21 (95%)	9 of 9 (100%)

Committee Membership Summary

Date	Description
2013-2014	BOT (Chair), Executive (Chair), Executive Compensation (Chair), Academic Affairs (Chair), Finance, Trusteeship
2012-2013	BOT (Chair), Executive (Chair), Executive Compensation (Chair), Academic Affairs (Chair), Finance, Trusteeship
2011-2012	BOT (Chair), Executive (Chair), Executive Compensation (Chair), Finance, Trusteeship

University Involvement Summary

Date	Description
2013-2014	Trustee Carnival I DePaul Rodeo I Whistle Stop Tour I Theatre Gala I Classroom Presentation I White House Groundbreaking
2012-2013	Senate President Lunch I New Trustee Dinner I Trustee BBQ I Douglas Debates I Graduation Ceremonies I Ice Cream Social
2011-2012	Pie Eating Contest I DePaul Student Festival I Trustee Carnival I Classroom Presentation I Graduation Ceremonies I School of Music Concert

Engagement Relative to Other Trustees
Ranks each factor on a scale of 1 (lowest) to 10 (highest) of the trustees engagement relative to other current trustees

Category	2013-2014 Ranking	2012-2013 Ranking	2011-2012 Ranking
Philanthropy	8.3	7.6	7.7
Board Participation	9.0	9.3	10.0
University Participation	10.0	10.0	9.0

Figure 3.8   Individual Board Member Evaluation Sheet

EVALUATION OF BOARD MEETING EFFECTIVENESS

Because full board and board member performance assessments are typically conducted only once every few years, it may take quite a while before performance problems are identified and resolved. Therefore, boards are taking the opportunity to do more frequent performance check-ins by conducting evaluations of board and committee meetings.

These assessments are designed to be completed in a few minutes and generally focus on whether the meeting was effective and productive. Board leaders work with the CEO to evaluate the results of these quick assessments and bring the results, along with ideas for improvements, to the next meeting. Ideas can then be tested at subsequent meetings, and those that are effective can be adopted.

Board meeting evaluations assess the quality of an organization's governance.

Evaluating board meetings has several benefits. First, it provides immediate feedback that can be acted on quickly to improve meeting value. It also reinforces that improving performance is part of the board's ongoing responsibilities and helps build momentum for continuous improvement. Finally, it shows board members that their input is important and is acted upon quickly by board leaders.

Evaluation of board and committee meetings should focus on both meeting process and outcome. Sample questions to assess meeting effectiveness include:

- Were there specific objectives for the meeting, and did the agenda support them?

- Were the most important items at the front of the agenda?

- Did the meeting start and end on time?

- Were all members encouraged to participate?

These are the areas in which you can expect to be evaluated. Having a solid understanding of how you will be evaluated can help you position yourself to make a positive impression on the board both individually and as part of the team.

- Was material distributed enough in advance to allow for thoughtful review and preparation?

- Did the board spend more time dealing with the future than the past?

FINANCIAL CONTRIBUTIONS

It is often said that nonprofit board members are expected to contribute time, treasure, and talents. "Nurses need to know—particularly when serving on nonprofit boards—that they will be expected to contribute not only through their time but also through financial support of the organization," said Daniel Pesut, who was surprised by the expectation when he first sat on a nonprofit board. "We don't talk about it much. It's more tacit instead of explicit."

> I guess I was pretty naïve about the whole notion of philanthropic contributions to a board, until I got on the Sigma board. It's not just a service that you give, but it's the financial commitment and an expectation about your philanthropic activity in terms of sustainability of the organization that becomes important.

The phrase "give or get" is often applied to this financial contribution. The board member can either give their own money or help get money from other sources to meet their financial obligations.

REFERENCES

Beavor, K. (2014). Right from the start: What your nonprofit board needs in three easy tables. Retrieved from http://www.bridgespan.org/Publications-and-Tools/ Hiring-Nonprofit-Leaders/Recruiting-Board-Members/Right-from-the-Start-What-Your-Board-Needs.aspx#.VcUiLflVhBc

Gauss, J. & Valentine, S. (2013). Recruiting the right mix. *Trustee* (June, 2013).

Holtschneider, D. H. (May/June 2013). The incalculable benefits of revitalizing your board. *Trusteeship Magazine.* May/June 2013. http://agb.org/trusteeship/2013/5/ incalculable-benefits-revitalizing-your-board

Landen, R. (2014). Another year of pay hikes for hospital CEOs. *Modern Healthcare* (August 9, 2014).

4

TOP COMPETENCIES FOR SUCCESSFUL BOARD SERVICE

Board members who are passionate about the mission bring energy and urgency to the board. In addition to that passion, strong communication skills are very important to truly hearing what other board members are saying, as well as effectively contributing your own point of view and knowledge.

A certain level of financial literacy is a must. Nurses do not need to be accountants to succeed in a board role, but they do need to have an understanding of where the money comes from, where it goes, and what that means to the organization. Whether a nonprofit board or a corporate board, money is very important. No money, no mission.

Passion and communication skills are necessary for board membership, but successful board service is built on a foundation of other strong competencies, including finance, strategy, and risk-taking.

Most nurses will not be seeking to serve on a public corporate board, at least not as their first foray into the boardroom. Nurses are quite likely, though, to seek—and attain—a spot on a healthcare organization's board. In 2009, the American Hospital Association Center for Healthcare Governance convened a Blue Ribbon Panel on Trustee Core Competencies. The panel identified two sets of core competencies for trustees of hospitals and health systems.

The first set includes knowledge and skill competencies in three areas: healthcare delivery and performance, business and finance, and human resources. The panel suggested that all boards, regardless of the kind of hospital or system they govern, should have some members with these competencies.

The second set of competencies includes personal capabilities that the panel recommended should be sought in all board members. These competencies describe the kinds of behaviors board members should be able to demonstrate. See Figure 4.1.

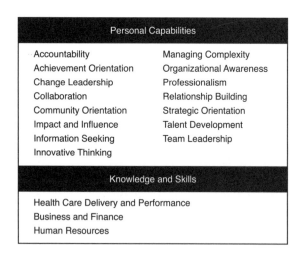

Figure 4.1   Individual Trustee Core Competencies

The panel's recommendations were based on interviews of board members, executives, research, and literature. The insights of the board members interviewed for this book support these competencies. What does it take to succeed as a board member? Take a look at the key skills through the eyes of these leaders.

AN UNDERSTANDING OF FINANCE

Because of the fiduciary responsibility of the board, having financial expertise is essential. Most boards have members with backgrounds as a chief financial officer (CFO), certified public accountant (CPA), and so on, and these experts lead the Audit and Finance committees. Still, all board members need some understanding of finance.

The nurse experts that I interviewed varied in their views regarding the importance of financial expertise for nurses. An understanding of finance is important today, says Therese Fitzpatrick, an executive and principal clinical strategist. "Not just finance related to operations, but understanding pretty complex finance in terms of partnerships and risk. How do you do the financing of complex real estate deals? The financing for the purchase of medical practices? It's more than just doing a budget. Maybe 15 years ago that was enough. It isn't any longer."

But, say others, nurses—or any nonfinancial board members—are not expected to be financial experts.

"You don't have to be an accountant; you just have to be well-versed," says Susan Hassmiller, an executive and nursing advisor.

Board members need to be able to read and understand the profit and loss statement (P&L). They don't need to understand organizational accounting or auditing.

That means understanding the basics and, at the highest level—which is where the board operates—understanding where the money comes from and where it goes.

Nurses likely have experience balancing their checkbook, managing a household budget, applying for mortgages and other loans, and so on. That is really all that is needed from a board level perspective. Chances are good that at least one member of the board is an accountant or has financial expertise. They will lead in the areas of finance and auditing.

Too many nurses, says Linda Procci, retired COO and VP, hold themselves back from board service because they say things like, "I can't be on a board because I've never been a leader—I've never done major budget planning." When she hears this, "I say 'Really? How much money do you make? Do you manage your bills? Do you invest in your 401k plan? Okay, then you've had experience. It's just that the numbers are significantly bigger!'"

Joanne Disch, former academic executive, professor, and seasoned board member, notes that nurses bring value from a financial standpoint in a more qualitative way as well. "Sometimes I think that people who only have financial acumen really don't understand how you calculate other costs such as reputational costs or loss of morale or community pushback. I think nurses bring this idea that, yes, the traditional way of looking at finances is necessary, but it's not enough."

Laurie Benson, CEO and entrepreneur, says, "What I have found to be very effective is scheduling an appointment with the executive director, president,

Find a CEO willing to fill in some of the blanks of your financial understanding.

or CEO—whoever is running the company—ask them to walk you through your financials. What were the assumptions made about this budget, what are the trends, where do you consistently have variances, how does this link to the strategic plan?'"

It's important to link the organization's performance to the strategy.

HEALTHCARE-SPECIFIC FINANCE

Healthcare finance is unique and often confusing. Board members are often shocked to learn that hospitals are dependent upon physicians for patients, and these same physicians admit patients to competing hospitals. Board members are confused by the huge difference between hospital charges and actual reimbursement. The fact that different insurers pay different amounts for the same procedures is also confusing.

The United States spends roughly 17% of its gross domestic product (GDP) on healthcare, according to World Bank data (n.d.). By 2018, national healthcare expenditures are expected to reach $4.4 trillion, which is more than double 2007 spending (Centers for Medicare & Medicaid Services, 2008) and will represent 20.3% of GDP. As a steward for the organization you represent, your understanding of finance can help you make better decisions that can positively affect both the quality and the cost of care.

In 2013, the U.S. annual healthcare expenditures reached $2.9 trillion, or $9,255 per person (Centers for Medicare & Medicaid Services). This amount is equivalent to 17.4% of the GDP. Based on World Bank data (2013), U.S. healthcare spending is almost twice as much as other countries spend. According to the Centers for Medicare & Medicaid Services (2013), the major sources of funds for healthcare are:

- **Medicare:** Medicare spending, which represented 20 percent of national health spending in 2013, grew 3.4 percent to $585.7 billion, a slowdown from growth of 40 percent in 2012. This slowdown was attributed largely to slower enrollment growth and impacts of the Affordable Care Act (ACA) and sequestration. Per-enrollee spending in 2013 grew at about the same rate as 2012.

- **Medicaid:** Total Medicaid spending (15 percent of national health spending) grew 6.1 percent in 2013 to $449.4 billion, an acceleration from 4.0 percent growth in 2012. Federal Medicaid expenditures increased 6.2 percent in 2013, while state and local Medicaid expenditures grew 5.9 percent.

- **Private Health Insurance:** Overall, premiums reached $961.7 billion in 2013 (representing a 33 percent share of national health spending), and increased 2.8 percent, slower than the 40 percent growth in 2012. The net cost ratio for private health insurance—the difference between premiums and benefits as a share of premiums—was 120 percent in 2013, the same as in 2012. Private health insurance enrollment increased 0.7 percent to 189.3 million in 2013, but was still 8.2 million lower than in 2007.

- **Out-of-Pocket:** Out-of-pocket spending, which accounted for 12 percent of national health spending, grew 3.2 percent in 2013 to $339.4 billion, a deceleration from growth of 3.6 percent in 2012. (Centers for Medicare & Medicaid Services, 2013).

Next to the government payors, the next largest group of payors is private insurers. A small percentage of the money comes through *private payors*—those individuals without insurance who pay for their own care out of pocket. The cost of uninsured patients' care is borne by the hospital itself through *charity care* or *uncompensated care*. As of March 2015, the U.S. uninsured rate was 11.9% (Gallup, 2015).

Where does the money go in healthcare? Primarily to hospitals. About one-third (32%) of U.S. healthcare dollars is spent on hospital care. The next highest area of expenditure is physicians and clinics at 20%, with 9% going toward prescription drugs. Surprisingly, nursing home care represents a relatively small percentage (5%) of these expenditures, as does dental care (7%) (Millman, 2014).

NONPROFIT HOSPITALS

Of the 5,724 hospitals in the U.S., 2,903 are nonprofit and 1,045 are community hospitals where the state or local government is the owner, not investors (Dunn & Becker, 2013).

Nonprofits need to quantify the value they provide to their communities. Usually, best-practice hospitals do this in the form of an annual report of benefits that includes things such as free or uncompensated care as well as flu shot clinics or blood pressure screenings. An analysis of a hospital's community benefit reports indicates that nurses provide many of the community benefits through their work in the community, churches, and schools. Hospitals need to be able to show to the communities they serve the benefits they are providing so that they can justify and maintain their nonprofit status.

Nonprofit status means that hospitals don't have to pay federal income taxes and property taxes. In exchange for their nonprofit status, hospitals are expected to benefit the communities they serve.

INVESTOR-OWNED HOSPITALS

Not all hospitals are nonprofit, though. Roughly 1,025 of the 5,724 U.S. hospitals (approximately 18%) are investor-owned for-profit hospitals (Dunn & Becker, 2013). They are traded on the stock exchange, and the main goal of these hospitals is to provide shareholder value. Just as you make a choice to buy stock in corporations, you might also buy shares of stock in for-profit hospitals or chains of hospitals. Unlike nonprofit hospitals, investor-owned hospitals pay taxes.

Investor-owned hospitals run just like any other publicly owned hospital. There are board members who are elected by the shareholders and who must comply with all rules and regulations that would govern any publicly traded organization. For-profit healthcare and university boards are obligated to the same rules and regulations as any corporate board. Although there are differences in financing and tax status, for-profit healthcare and education organizations are held accountable to the same accrediting organizations. They are held accountable for the same patient and student outcomes as their nonprofit equivalents. Financing and tax status should not be used to measure moral superiority. Do your homework and ask questions before you invoke any moral judgments.

GOVERNMENTAL HOSPITALS

Yet another type of healthcare structure comprises governmental healthcare organizations. These might include anything from Veterans Administration (VA) hospitals to state university hospitals. Their board structures generally vary significantly from most hospital systems.

Some communities have county hospitals—or, in some larger metropolitan areas, such as New York City—even city hospitals. The government owns these and, of course, they often don't pay taxes. In fact, in some cases, they may have the ability to tax. Some university hospitals are a taxing entity, so they really can add to the tax structure.

The governor usually appoints board members in these types of state-controlled organizations. In some states, such as Florida and California, members of the public actually run for election to the public hospital board. In the case of city hospitals, a mayor will typically appoint the hospital board members. In some states with county-owned hospitals, the county judge or the county board members appoint hospital board members. Nurses should make themselves available for appointment to these governmental healthcare organization's boards.

HEALTHCARE TRENDS

More and more healthcare organizations are reporting their measures of efficiency and effectiveness in their annual reports to stakeholders (IBM, 2012).

TRANSPARENCY

The ability to be transparent requires some form of reporting mechanisms—some type of scorecard or performance report to indicate how the organization is performing.

Transparency means that organizations are open in their operations and will publicly report information about how they are performing to their various stakeholders.

HEALTHCARE TRENDS

In an industry governed by so many regulations and that has such an impact on the lives of millions of Americans, it is not surprising that people want to know how their healthcare organizations are performing. What are the quality levels? How are they doing financially? How much benefit are they providing to the communities they serve?

In late 2008, the American Hospital Association convened a Blue Ribbon Panel, which issued a report that explored the need for hospitals to create transparent reporting mechanisms. Rather than hide errors from the board and from the community, there needed to be broad and open communication and more transparent metrics.

Whoever the stakeholders are, the key point is that it is essential to keep them informed about the state of the organization. That may mean sending internal monthly performance reports to the managers and medical staff. It may mean giving updates to the community through a community newsletter or website. For many hospitals, it means generating annual reports to the community outlining the benefit provided by the hospital to the community.

Stakeholders are right in holding the board responsible for transparency and high-quality operations. All organizations—nonprofit, for-profit, advisory, and nursing associations—must focus on providing regular, clear performance reports to their stakeholders.

HEALTHCARE TRENDS

A recent development is that hospitals that participate in the Medicare program are required to share specific quality, cost, and performance data. Many private insurers are also requiring similar performance data. Hospitals should provide quarterly performance reports for their stakeholders—typically trustees, employees, physicians, patients, the community, and so on. Different types of hospitals also have other unique stakeholders. Religious hospitals, for instance, have a religious organization that sponsors them, and teaching hospitals have a university or college as a key stakeholder.

USING SCORECARDS

Scorecards that focus on a few key metrics are the most helpful in driving organizational performance. The series of scorecards that follow includes the source of the benchmark and whether it internal to the hospital or from an outside source. Is it preferable that the results are higher or lower? How is the organization doing on the metric? Is it as expected, better, or worse? By focusing on a few key metrics, the board, management, and employees are unified in their understanding of what's important to the organization.

I was chair of the Silver Cross Hospital board that is now in New Lenox, Illinois. We had the motto, "If you can measure it, you can move it." Through the use of quality and finance metrics, Silver Cross achieved Solucient Top 100 Hospitals status for seven consecutive years.

HEALTHCARE TRENDS

In its 2013–2018 Futurescan report (ACHE, 2013), the American College of Healthcare Executives indicates that boards will elevate quality from an oversight function to a strategic priority and will devote at least 20% of their meeting time to discussions of quality-related issues, including quality objectives in the CEO's performance evaluation.

Figure 4.2 is an example of a scorecard that reports metrics that this particular hospital has defined as key operational metrics. Because emergency department (ED) admissions are a key driver of hospital admissions, there is a focus on ED visits, which on the scorecard in Figure 4.2, are better than expected. Most hospitals monitor their monthly inpatient admissions as a metric of market share, among others. This hospital's admissions are right on target.

	Benchmark	Preferred	Worse than Expected ★	As Expected ★★	Better than Expected ★★★
Average Monthly ED Visits	Internal	Higher	≤4,692	4,742	4,914
Average Monthly Inpatient Admissions (Newborns Excluded)	Internal	Higher	≤1,453	1,467	≥1,478
Medicare Length of Stay Days	Solucient	Lower	4.53	4.4	4.32≥
FTE's per Adjusted Occupied Bed	Solucient	Lower	3.77	3.73 – 3.67	3.66≥

Figure 4.2 Sample Metrics

Medicare pays the same amount of money regardless of whether a patient stays 3 days or 5. Obviously, then, it is better for the hospital's bottom line— and often for the patient, too—if the

The Medicare length of stay (LOS) metric is key to a hospital's cost position.

patient's stay is shorter. Most hospitals monitor this metric very closely. Although this scorecard indicates that the 4.5 days LOS metric is worse than expected for this particular hospital, it is actually a very low and very good Medicare length of stay nationally.

FTEs per adjusted occupied bed (AOB) is a metric that describes how many employees there are per patient. Given that employees are the largest percentage of a hospital's budget, this is clearly an essential metric.

Adjusted occupied beds (AOBs) are hospital total gross patient revenue ÷ hospital inpatient revenue x occupied beds.

Hospitals use AOBs as a way of building in volume for things such as clinics and ED because they indicate how the entire organization is performing. AOB is an indication of efficiency. The board and management need to know how many people it requires to get the job done.

Two key financial metrics are displayed on the scorecard in Figure 4.3: variance and surgical volume. Variance from annual budget is extremely important, and this hospital is right on its target.

	Benchmark	Preferred	Worse than Expected ★	As Expected ★★	Better than Expected ★★★
Annual Operating Income Variance From Budget	Budget	Higher	≤($600,000)	**$4,000**	≥$300,000
Average Monthly Surgical Procedure Volume (Inpatient and Outpatient)	Internal	Higher	**1,113**	1,146	≥1,154

Figure 4.3   Additional Metrics

The board needs to look at the organization as a whole and needs to review each of the programs in the organization. For example, this particular scorecard is focused on surgical volume. Surgery can be an important source of revenue for the entire organization when done effectively and efficiently. If there is poor-quality surgery resulting in readmissions or even lawsuits, the hospital will lose money and credibility. If surgical services are run efficiently, with low costs and high quality, surgical services can be a huge asset.

Typically when hospitals initially use scorecards, they focus on areas with the most opportunity for growth or improvement. It is not unusual to optimize operations in one clinical area and then change the focus to another. Simple scorecards are a valuable resource for the board to monitor organizational performance.

Too often, says Susan Hassmiller, senior adviser for nursing for the Robert Wood Johnson Foundation, nurses will dismiss the value they might bring to a board role, often over concerns about their lack of expertise in the financial area. It's important to get beyond this, she says. "Your perspective, your talent, and your skill may not be accounting and finance, but you need to focus on what you *can* bring. That's the beauty of the board; it brings together people with unique perspectives."

If an organization monitors its budget monthly, there is time to adjust for periods of poor performance. When organizations monitor their budgets less frequently, there is less opportunity to make corrections.

Nurses can be extremely helpful in creating, interpreting, and helping other board members with the use of scorecards.

SIGNIFICANT RESPONSIBILITIES

As a member of a healthcare organization board, you have responsibility for the financial health of the organization you serve. Finance is one of two responsibilities that hospital board members have under the law:

1. The responsibility for the quality of care

2. The responsibility for the organization's financial viability

The responsibilities—and risks—of serving as a board member have increased significantly over the past several years.

Directors and officers insurance (D&O) policies function as management errors and omissions liability insurance covering claims resulting from managerial decisions that have adverse financial consequences.

Board members must rely on the management team in the organization to keep them informed of the organization's financial performance. The management team will prepare a budget and a long-term strategy. The board will be asked to approve both the budget and the strategy, which requires that they understand what they entail and how they relate to each other.

When a board reviews its budget and strategic plan, it should not look at these two documents in isolation, but consider how well they are aligned. For instance, if one of the stated objectives in the hospital's strategic plan is to be the number-one orthopedic care provider in its service area, the board will need to ensure that there are resources identified to achieve this objective. If the hospital plans to be the number-one orthopedic provider in its service area, has it set aside dollars in the budget to stay up to date with the most advanced orthopedic equipment? Are there funds designed to recruit top orthopedic positions? What about

All organizations, whether for profit or nonprofit, should provide their board members with directors and officers (D&O) insurance to protect them from liability for claims made against them while serving on a board of directors.

The *strategic plan* outlines steps for both the short-term and long: generally, what is going to happen this year along with the planning forecast for the next 3 years.

providing expert nursing as well as physical and occupational therapy professionals? The board must align its actions with its words.

Board members also have a responsibility to monitor financial performance outcomes for the organization. Typically, the board will get monthly financial reports. These reports should indicate the financial stability of the organization and identify any potential risks to the organization's financial standing. Are the hospital's actual expenses and revenue closely aligned with the budgeted expenses and revenue? Is the hospital performing better or worse than it did last quarter or last year? These are simple financial metrics that are easily understood.

Finally, board members need to ensure that adequate internal controls are in place and functioning properly to serve as checks and balances for the organization's financial performance as well as to provide early warning signs that might indicate the need for further investigation or a change in strategy or direction.

Board members need to determine whether the organization has adequate internal controls—*checks and balances*—to ensure that financial processes are ethical and in compliance with laws and regulations.

Checks and balances in nonprofit organizations, which most hospitals are, include requirements related to obtaining competitive bids for certain types of expenditures. So, if the hospital was constructing a new building or contracting for a new service—housekeeping or landscaping, for instance—the board would need to ensure that the process involved competitive bids from vendors and contractors before the project was awarded. There should be internal controls related to things such as executive expense accounts, petty cash accounts, and irregular expenditures. The organization's external auditor can assist the board in identifying areas for key internal controls, or checks and balances. It is the board's major legal responsibility to select, monitor, and evaluate the external auditor.

Board members should monitor the organization's effectiveness and efficiency.

Effectiveness focuses on the achievement of mission, vision, and goals. *Efficiency* focuses on the appropriate use of resources.

Some of the scorecard metrics discussed earlier report data such as the ratio of caregivers to patients. It can help to have comparisons of how other hospitals are performing to provide a frame of reference—a *benchmark*—for comparison. In most states, you can get information from the state hospital association to look at metrics such as cost per case: For example, how is our cost per case compared with other healthcare providers in our market, or in the state, or even on a national basis?

Although it can be helpful to have comparative data from other organizations, it is important to determine whether the organization is performing better than it was last year, last quarter, or even last month.

Identified inefficiencies can then be raised as potential areas of strategic focus as part of the hospital's planning and continuous improvement process.

The best comparator is the organization against its own past performance. This information can help you identify areas in which the organization may be more or less efficient.

AN UNDERSTANDING OF STRATEGY

Most organizations want to improve in some way, notes Linda Procci, former hospital VP and COO. That requires strategy. Procci indicates that nurses have valuable experiences they may not even recognize. "How different is this from the performance improvement projects you're running on your nursing unit? Making these kinds of comparisons is really helpful in terms of building confidence." You know more than you think you know and have more to offer than you likely realize.

Strategic planning can be looked at from different perspectives that include both what the process is, as well as what it is designed to accomplish. In their monograph *Successful Strategic Planning: The Board's Role*, authors Gene O'Dell and John Combes (2009) define strategic planning as a discipline that enables the board and leadership to evaluate the current environment as well as the organization's position in it, and then craft a plan to achieve the mission. This view of planning describes key steps involved in the process itself.

Strategic planning expert Nate Kaufman takes a different view (2006). He defines strategic planning in terms of what it *should* accomplish. Kaufman says that strategic planning is the process of developing true competencies to deal with market opportunities.

There are many steps involved in a successful strategic planning process. They include:

- **Gaining buy-in** from key participants and other stakeholders, including the CEO, board chair, clinical leaders, and other stakeholders who are asked to participate. It is also important for the board to establish a Strategic Planning committee to help guide the process. This committee often includes board members and key executives.

- **Conducting an environmental assessment** is another key step in the planning process. Understanding both the external and the internal environment facing the organization can then help those involved in the planning process to analyze the organization's strengths and weaknesses and identify the opportunities and threats facing the hospital.

- **Developing both planning and financial assumptions** that guide the process and link the plan with the resources necessary to achieve it.

- **Developing a strategic framework** (after the assumptions are in place) that includes the organization's vision, mission, and values, and allows participants in the process to set strategies to achieve them.

- **Establishing performance measures** to allow the board and organizational leaders to work together to periodically assess progress toward achieving the plan.

Although the board does not actually conduct the planning process, it does have many responsibilities throughout the process. These key elements of the strategic framework drive goals and strategies.

A key role for the board is to establish or revise the organization's vision, mission, and values.

The board is also responsible for guiding the planning process. Boards can do this through existing committees, such as an executive or a Strategic Planning committee, or by establishing a Strategic Planning steering committee.

Ask yourself: How are the stakeholders of any organization brought into the planning?

Because boards are accountable to the organization's stakeholders, the board must ensure that stakeholders provide input and feedback to the planning process. Boards should ensure that the planning process seeks out a variety of diverse perspectives about where the organization is today and where it should go in the future.

One of the key roles that a board plays throughout the planning process is to ask questions and challenge planning assumptions and conclusions. Boards should ask management to explain why the organization's goals, strategies, and direction make sense. Kaufman (2006) also suggests that boards make sure the strategic plan is not merely a collection of pet projects of either the board or management.

The board is responsible for setting overall strategic direction and performance targets or goals for the organization. The board then works with the organization's leaders to establish specific strategies to achieve the goals. The board and organization leaders' sharing the responsibility for developing strategies to achieve plan goals helps build shared ownership in successful implementation of the plan.

After the plan is completed, the board sets implementation in motion by approving the plan. Throughout the year, it is the board's job to monitor plan progress and, at least once per year, evaluate performance against the plan. Ongoing monitoring of progress toward accomplishing the plan is essential to making sure there are no surprises when it comes to evaluating plan performance. The board needs to know as soon as possible if unexpected events will either positively or negatively affect intended outcomes. To ensure that the board and leadership are aligned in achieving plan goals, the board should also tie executive performance and compensation to the organization's strategic performance.

Organizational leaders are responsible for working with the board to start the planning process. An important first step is to establish a timeline for the process and to identify key participants. The timeline should lay out critical steps in the planning process and who is responsible for completing them. Organizational leaders also are responsible for setting strategies with the board to achieve plan goals.

After plan goals and strategies are in place, organizational leaders then develop tactics and business plans to achieve them. There may be more than one way to achieve a goal or implement a strategy. Tactics or business plans are about making choices because they set out the specific steps organizational leaders are committing to take to reach the goals.

No plan will be successful without resources to support it. A key responsibility of organizational management is to ensure that budgets and other needed resources, such as time and personnel, are tied to the plan to support implementation. It is primarily the responsibility of the organization's executives and other leaders to execute the plan. The plan's success is the joint responsibility of the board and the management team. DePaul University is superb at tying the strategic plan into the board's activities. At each DePaul board meeting, the CEO and board chair refer to the strategic plan in a way that makes it clear that the plan is guiding the activities and ensuring its achievement.

AN ABILITY TO IDENTIFY RISKS

The board has a responsibility to identify, monitor, and *ameliorate*, or remove, risks for the organization. Enterprise risk management is a board responsibility that board members must take very seriously.

Some of the common risks in today's healthcare environment are explained in the following section.

It is essential for the board and management to spend time identifying the current and potential risks that might impact the organization and create plans to avoid or remedy the risks.

NEW BUSINESS RELATIONSHIPS

As challenges and changes to the healthcare environment are faced, healthcare board members and leadership teams must face them and successfully implement policies, plans, and procedures to help the organization thrive, no matter the challenge. An example was the rollout of the U.S.'s Affordable Care Act (ACA). Boards and administrators wondered, "Are we really going to be able to partner with the best doctors? Are we going to be able to create a way of competing on value and then sharing the money earned in a way that all parties feel is equitable? How will we implement bundled payments?" Challenges and changes are inevitable, but they also create opportunities for the nimble and responsive organizations.

NEW COMPETITION

Healthcare competition is emerging from new areas. For instance, even small hospitals are now facing the risk of prestigious organizations such as Mayo Clinic and the Cleveland Clinic moving into much smaller and rural communities. So, for some hospitals, they have to consider whether their little community hospitals can compete with these nationally renowned organizations.

HEALTHCARE TRENDS

There is new competition from insurance companies, pharmacies, and large discount stores as they move into the primary care arena. They're offering services that traditionally have taken place in physicians' offices, such as immunizations, tests for strep or ear infections, and other sorts of "minute clinic" types of services. Consumers can visit the pharmacy and see a healthcare provider—often, a nurse practitioner (NP)—get a prescription, and get discharged quickly and efficiently. It's an entirely new kind of competition that healthcare organizations have not faced before. Many boards will try to determine whether they should compete with, partner with, or duplicate the competitor's services.

KEY TALENT AVAILABILITY

Healthcare organizations have numerous risks to their ability to recruit and retain the right kind of executive talent. Many CEOs want to be the CEO of their own little hospital. According to the American Hospital Association (2015), 3,144 hospitals of the 5,686 registered hospitals are part of a multihospital or diversified single hospital system—roughly 55%. Will hospitals be able to recruit good talent interested in running smaller and potentially less significant (in the eyes of the system head) organizations?

HEALTHCARE TRENDS

Certain types of nursing positions are especially vulnerable to talent shortage: for example, nurses who are skilled at discharge planning. Hospitals are not getting reimbursed for readmissions as they always had been. If they cannot discharge the patient effectively, maintain care at home, and the patient is readmitted, the hospital is at risk of losing significant amounts of money. In addition to expertise in discharge planning, many more expert nurses will be necessary for the expanding areas of home care and nursing home care. There has been a significant rise in demand for nurses who can work in primary care settings and also in areas of health promotion and disease prevention. The ability to attract and retain advance practice nurses will be a challenge for many healthcare organizations.

As the largest segment of the U.S. health workforce, recruiting and retaining nurses needs to be a top priority for all healthcare boards. The Patient Protection and Affordable Care Act (2010), the Institute of Medicine (2011), and the Robert Wood Johnson Foundation (2015) all point out the key role that

Having a nurse on a healthcare board can be extremely helpful in identifying issues related to the recruitment, development, and retention of nursing and other types of healthcare talent.

quality nursing care plays in improved patient outcomes and reduced costs, which, in turn, can reduce the potential financial exposure to hospitals and healthcare organizations.

Healthcare organizations have been the primary employer of nurses, but now they will have to compete with pharmaceutical companies, insurers, stand-alone clinics, large corporations in wellness management, and other employers.

CHANGING PHYSICIAN RELATIONSHIPS

Healthcare organizations are at risk in their physician relationships. Today's physician's world is much different than it was just a few years ago and certainly different from what many of them imagined for their careers when they entered medical school. Some physicians were essentially entrepreneurs when they went into medical practice. They ran their own business in their own office. They often worked 60 to 80 hours per week as they built their practice. Now systems are taking these independent entrepreneurial physicians and bringing them into their systems as employees. They are now subject to numerous business regulations and human resource rules for the first time in their careers, and this presents a risk to their productivity and job satisfaction.

The move to bundled payments presents great risk to the organization's relationships with its medical staff members. There are few examples of successful functioning under bundled payments. Like all new payment methodologies, there will be errors and problems and great opportunities for learning. Boards must communicate their intentions to be fair and work closely for the success of both the physicians and the healthcare organization.

AGING PHYSICAL PLANTS

Operating a hospital and keeping the physical plant up to date is very expensive. With declining inpatient visits, many hospitals are finding themselves with more beds—and related costs—than they need. Today, patients in beds are somewhat of a liability unless the patient is in that bed for a short period of time and having an expensive procedure. Hospitals are forced to make tough decisions about closing some of their beds. Is it possible that hospitals with fewer beds have shorter lengths of stay (LOS)? Common sense might argue that if the physician has to discharge a patient to clear a bed in order to admit another patient, that is what will happen. If the physician can keep the existing patient and easily admit a new patient, there is less likelihood that that patient will be discharged rapidly.

When identifying risks related to their aging physical plants, boards must also consider investing in nonhospital venues of care. Is their organization prepared to care for their stakeholders in clinics, homes, and other community sites? Is the best approach to mitigating this risk to invest in new venues or partner with existing organizations? There is rarely a single correct approach to risk, but all approaches involve vigorous debate and discussion.

BOARD COMPETENCY AND PREPAREDNESS

Hospitals are also facing risks related to their boards. Do the current board members have the skill sets required to move the healthcare organization forward in a dynamic environment? Do they have skills needed for merger and acquisitions?

In addition to these broad categories of risks, each organization will identify, monitor, and manage its own risks. These risks are real and dynamic. The environment, internal and external, is changing continually. Board members need to be adept at seeing—and foreseeing—the risks that may impact the organizations and create processes for enterprise risk management.

Boards need nurses who have worked in home care and long-term care to help them decide whether they should be moving into the home care and long-term care areas of healthcare.

REFERENCES

American Hospital Association Center for Healthcare Governance. (2009). Competency-based governance enters the healthcare boardroom. Author. http://www.americangovernance.com/resources/monographs/11-governance-boardroom.shtml

Centers for Medicare & Medicaid Services. (2013). National health expenditures 2013 highlights. Author. https://www.cms.gov/Research-Statistics-Data-and-Systems/Statistics-Trends-and-Reports/NationalHealthExpendData/Downloads/highlights.pdf

Centers for Medicare & Medicaid Services. (2008). National health expenditure projections 2008-2018. Author. http://www.cms.gov/Research-Statistics-Data-and-Systems/Statistics-Trends-and-Reports/NationalHealthExpendData/downloads/proj2008.pdf

Committee for The Robert Wood Johnson Foundation Initiative on the Future of Nursing, at the Institute of Medicine. (2011). *The future of nursing: Leading change, advancing health*. http://www.thefutureofnursing.org/IOM-Report

Dunn, L. & Becker, S. (July 23, 2013). 50 things to know about the hospital industry. *Becker's Hospital Review*. http://www.beckershospitalreview.com/hospital-management-administration/50-things-to-know-about-the-hospital-industry.html

Gallup. (April 3, 2015). In U.S., uninsured rate dips to 11.9% in first quarter. Author. http://www.gallup.com/poll/182348/uninsured-rate-dips-first-quarter.aspx

IBM. (2012). The value of analytics in healthcare: From insights to outcomes. Author. http://www.ibm.com/smarterplanet/global/files/the_value_of_analytics_in_healthcare.pdf

Kaufman, N. (2006). *Why many strategic planning efforts fail.* In E-Briefings: A summary of news, resources, and events. The Governance Institute: Vol. 3, No. 2, March 2006.

Millman, J. (December 3, 2014). Here's exactly how the United States spends $2.9 trillion on health care. *The Washington Post.* http://www.washingtonpost.com/blogs/wonkblog/wp/2014/12/03/heres-exactly-how-the-united-states-spends-2-9-trillion-on-health-care/

O'Dell, G. J. & Combes, J. R. (2009). *Successful strategic planning: The board's role.* American Hospital Association's Center for Healthcare Governance: Chicago, IL.

Patient Protection and Affordable Care Act of 2010, Public Law 111–148. http://housedocs.house.gov/energycommerce/ppacacon.pdf

Robert Wood Johnson Foundation. (2015). The value of nursing in building a culture of health (part 1, policy brief). http://www.rwjf.org/content/dam/farm/reports/issue_briefs/2015/rwjf419194

World Bank. (n.d.). World Health Organization global health expenditure database. Author. http://data.worldbank.org/indicator/SH.XPD.TOTL.ZS

5

PLANNING YOUR PATH TO BOARD SERVICE

Making a commitment to serve on a board should not be taken lightly. In "Recruiting the Right Mix," Gauss (2013) notes some questions that candidates may want to ask themselves when considering a board opportunity:

- What does this hospital or system's future look like?

- Is there a desire and commitment to change?

- Can I bring value to the organization and board? If so, why this organization in particular? Do I have the time?

- What are meeting attendance requirements?

- What is my donation commitment?

Finally, make sure that you are doing a critical assessment of the skills, experiences, and background that you have to bring to board service, as well as areas of opportunity for improvement. No candidate will have everything that it takes to be a success the first time on a board. In fact, even seasoned board members find that they are continually learning and growing through these experiences. This is a journey, not a destination.

You may be invited to join a board, as mentioned in Chapter 3, "What Nurses Need to Know to Get on Boards(s)." Or, you may come to board service via another, more proactive, avenue: seeking a membership.

Daniel Pesut, professor and experienced board leader, talks about the "red thread": a theme in your life. Be "intentional in terms of particular interests, values, and beliefs…How do [you] want to serve a greater purpose in terms of the kind of organizations that you commit to?"

YOUR STRENGTHS

One way to discover your strengths, says Pesut, is through a tool like the Gallup StrengthsFinder (https://www.gallupstrengthscenter.com/Home/en-US/Index).

"I attended a workshop a few months ago, and now what they're suggesting is that people string together those top five signature strengths into a personal mission statement. Not to look at them as separate individual strengths, but how do you link them together and what does that say about you in terms

"I really think that every nurse in America should know what their top five or top ten signature strengths and talents are and how those strengths and talents contribute to board leadership," Pesut says.

of the strengths that you would bring to an enterprise or a group process? I think knowing your strengths and talents and how to participate in a group is crucial for your own personal and professional well-being."

That self-awareness and understanding are a great launchpad for identifying the types of boards that are most aligned with your interests and where your service might be most impactful.

Reach out to those organizations that are aligned with your interests and passions. Several websites are devoted to matching volunteers to organizations that need their skills and abilities. For example, boardnetUSA (www.boardnetusa.org/public/home.asp) is a website devoted to matching potential board members with boards. The website is free to use, but the potential board member must complete a profile that includes the following:

- **Educational history:** School, city, state, major, degree

- **Employment history:** Employer, job title, city, state, length of employment

- **Nonprofit history:** Previous nonprofit work or volunteer experience, title, length of service

- **Heritage:** Gender, ethnicity, religion, birth year

- **Activities:** PTA, religion, politics, sports teams, advocacy

- **Board training:** Program attendance

- **Industry experience:** Which industries or sectors of your principle skills/expertise

- **Language:** Which ones you speak

- **Service interests:** Which types of organizations you would be interested in serving

- **Types of healthcare services:** Homecare, mental health, disease-specific, rehab, research

- **Types of human services:** Foster care, homelessness, immigrants, Boy/Girl Scouts, and seniors

- **Preference of operations budget size:** $100,000–200,000, $1M–$2M, not important

- **Preference of developmental stage:** Start-up, growth, steady state, transition

- **Commitment availability:** Hours per month available to devote to the board: < 4, 4–8, 9–12, 13–16

Regardless of whether you are interested in registering at this site, the questions posed there can help you gain clarity about your own interests. These are the types of considerations that you should have in mind as you are deciding whether board service is for you—and, if it is, what type of board you could most effectively serve.

YOUR INTERESTS

Consider your interests. What issues or populations are you really passionate about? Based on these interests, consider what organizations are working in that area. For example, if you have an interest in helping children, you might consider nonprofit organizations such as Girl Scouts, the Boys and Girls Club, or children's hospitals. All these organizations have boards.

And it is easy to go online to an organization's website and take a look at its key problems and accomplishments. What are the board's major challenges? Are your interests aligned with its mission, vision, and values? Can you demonstrate that you have the knowledge, skills, and abilities to help this organization achieve its mission and vision?

Take a look, also, at the annual report. All nonprofit organizations are required to file a Form 990, which is an IRS form for all organizations exempt from income taxes. The GuideStar organization (www.guidestar. org) is a free source for 990 forms.

The 990 form includes a great deal of information about the organization, including financial information related to endowments, grants, and so on. Healthcare organizations report their amount of charity care, bad debt, and community-building activities. The 990 form also includes information on the executive officer's compensation, including salaries, bonuses, and other benefits.

GuideStar (www.guidestar. org) is an information service that specializes in reporting on U.S. nonprofit organizations. Their mission is: "To revolutionize philanthropy by providing information that advances transparency, enables users to make better decisions, and encourages charitable giving."

After you review an organization's annual report, Form 990, and website, consider whether you are willing to devote between 4–10 hours per month to that organization. In addition to your time, all nonprofits need funding, and many expect board members to make an annual contribution. Sometimes they are quite explicit about this. I was on the board of a university, for instance, and that university expected its board members to "give or get" at least $10,000 per year. Is this an organization for which you are willing to get money for or give money to? Would you be willing to ask your friends, family members, and colleagues for support with donations or to purchase a ticket to a golf outing or an annual gala? Be honest with yourself.

"Give or get" means board members are expected to bring in money to the organization. Sometimes explicit but more often implicit, this can mean an outright donation or fundraising within your sphere of influence.

If your answers are all "yes," then this may be a board for you. If you are not willing to contribute your time, talent, and treasures to this organization, keep looking.

EVALUATE THE CURRENT BOARD MAKEUP

As you are preparing your paper introduction, take a look at the current board members of the organization and consider their experience. Most websites will list the board members and may also include bios. Even if they do not, it is worth your time to search online to see what you can find out about each board member. What skills do they bring to their roles? What skills seem to be lacking from the board makeup?

Chances are that you will find board members with financial backgrounds—auditors or CFOs. You may find some lawyers and bankers. However, you may not find any other clinicians. If you do, how is their clinical experience different from yours? How can you best communicate the unique skills you can bring to the board?

It is important that nurses distinguish themselves from existing members who are physicians. The public might think, "We have a doctor; why do we need a nurse, too?" Although physicians are highly specialized clinicians, they usually do not have the knowledge of organizational operations that many nurses possess. Most board members do not realize that nurses are the largest group of employees in most healthcare organizations and that they are closest to the patients, families, medical staff, and other employees. Nurses bring a valuable perspective that is usually different from that of physicians.

Maybe what you observe as you review the backgrounds of the current board members is that none of them possess quality and safety expertise, and you have been on the Quality Care committee of your hospital for several years—or you created the quality plan for your unit. Whatever your unique attributes are, you will want to reflect them in your bio or letter of introduction.

When you are being interviewed for the board membership, use the opportunity to ask questions regarding the core competencies that the board is looking for, the board evaluation process, and so on.

QUANTIFY YOUR EXPERIENCE

"Sitting on a board is like getting a job," says Linda Procci, retired VP and COO. "You need to think about what organizations are around you and if you could imagine yourself being passionate about their mission."

The process for landing a board role is, in many ways, very much like the process that you would use in a job search. You will, for example, need a resume that presents your qualifications. A one-pager like mine works best for this purpose (see Figure 5.1).

Because people who are reviewing the qualifications of potential board members do not have time to wade through the typical resume or curriculum vitae (CV), you have to mold your experience to fit board membership expectations.

The idea is to present your background in such a way that you position yourself as a desired member of the board on which you are seeking a position. As discussed in earlier chapters of this book, even if you do not have CEO or CFO experience, you likely have a wealth of background, experiences, and knowledge that you can use to put your best foot forward.

As you work to position yourself to present your bio/resume to the board, you will want to quantify, as best you can, your experiences. So, for instance, if you are trying to get a spot on the board of a children's hospital, you might consider all the interactions that you have had with children and their families over your nursing career. If you have been a nurse for 20 years, you may have interacted with 20,000 patients; you may have interacted with hundreds of physicians, hundreds of other nurses, therapists, and so on, over your career. Most of the other board members are unlikely to have had such in-depth experiences with the healthcare market that they serve. That is only one of the ways in which nurses can distinguish themselves.

Connie R. Curran,
EdD, RN, FAAN

Dr. Connie Curran is the CEO of Best on Board, a national organization focused on educating and certifying healthcare trustees. She was the founding executive director of C-Change, a national organization focused on the eradication of cancer. C-Change participants included the heads of federal and state governmental agencies, for-profit corporations, the motion picture industry, and nonprofit groups whose missions relate to cancer. There were approximately 150 C-Change participants. Former President George H. W. Bush and former First Lady Barbara Bush served as co-chairs, with Senator Dianne Feinstein serving as vice chair.

Dr. Curran was the founder, president, and chief executive officer of CurranCare, LLC, from 1995 to 2000. Curran Care was a national management and consulting services organization that delivered dynamic leadership to the healthcare industry. Cardinal Health acquired CurranCare, and she served as President of Cardinal Health Consulting Services, providing leadership to the approximately 200 consultants.

Dr. Curran has held a variety of executive positions in academic and academic healthcare organizations; she was the Chief Nursing Officer of Montefiore Medical Center in the Bronx, Vice President of the American Hospital Association and Dean at the Medical College of Wisconsin.

Dr. Curran is also one of the most prolific scholars in the field with more than 200 publications and several research programs to her credit. She served as the director of two of the most comprehensive national studies on staff recruitment, retention, and labor market participation. More recently she has co-authored books on hospital-physician integration, hospital redesign, and on optimized home care integration. She served as the editor of Nursing Economic$ for eighteen years. Her most recent book, Claiming the Corner Office: Executive Leadership Lessons for Nurses, was published in 2013.

She is a graduate of the Harvard Business School program for company owners and presidents. Dr. Curran has served on numerous corporate, privately held, and nonprofit boards. She is Chair of the Board of DeVry, Inc. She currently serves on the board of directors for Hospira, Inc., DePaul University, Chicago Lurie Children's Hospital, the University of Wisconsin Foundation, and was the former chairman of the board of Silver Cross Hospital.

Figure 5.1   Sample One-Sheet Bio/Resume.

MAKE CONNECTIONS

Gaining board-level experience, says Procci, is "really about putting yourself in a position where other people who are on boards know you're available and that you would be interested. It's all in who you know."

Joanne Disch, former academic executive, professor, and seasoned board member, agrees. "You never know when somebody's going to be in a position where they're looking for somebody who's really sharp, or somebody who's a really good nurse," she says. Your reputation truly does precede you. "You've got to be connected," she says. "You've got to volunteer, to get on committees. I tell new staff nurses, 'Join your Staffing committee on your patient care unit, find out what's going on in your institution. Volunteer to be a preceptor or somebody who's going to be on a work team.' You volunteer, you get involved."

Those with whom you have connected throughout your academic and professional career can also serve as great springboards to board service. As you are considering a board opportunity, you should review who the current board members are and whether you know any of them—or whether you have connections who may know them. If you do know someone on the board, that presents a wonderful opportunity. You can send that person an email and ask whether you could have a half hour of her time to discuss the board. Most people will give you that time, even if they do not know you. When you meet, share your passion and interests and what you believe you are particularly skilled at.

Even if you do not know any of the current board members, you may know someone who does and who could make an introduction. Chances are that if you work at a hospital, some of the people on your hospital's board know somebody on almost every other nonprofit board in the community. It is perfectly acceptable for you to go to one of your hospital's board members or one of your school board's members and ask whether they know someone on the board you are interested in. If they do, it is also acceptable to say, "I'm very interested in that organization, and I'd like to learn about becoming a member of the board."

If you do not know any members of the board you are interested in, it is still possible to make a connection.

Volunteering for the organization is a great way to meet some of the staff and observe the culture.

If you have a positive volunteer experience, you can pursue a board position. In this case, consider sending a letter— a real letter, not an email—to someone on the board, along with a copy of your one-page resume, indicating that you are interested in the board and would like to learn more. Request a short meeting to have a discussion. Very often, just that expression of interest from someone (like you) whose resume

Board meetings are not for quiet time. The more you talk and interact, the more you learn and expand your network, the more you expand your potential—both professionally and for the organization you are representing.

shows that s/he is skillful and whose personality shows commitment, will be enough to get you on the path to a board role.

After securing a seat on a board, notes Procci, it continues to be important to make connections. Many fail to do this, she says. "You need to make sure everybody knows who you are. Always talk at every meeting to help people remember who you are. And, of course, make sure you're going to the meetings prepared."

COMMUNITY OR ADVISORY BOARD OPPORTUNITIES

Many hospitals also have boards that they call *community* or *advisory boards*. These boards offer opportunities to serve in a less formal capacity and to gain experience that can serve as a training ground for a future board role with the hospital. The experiences that you will gain from participation on one of these types of boards will be very beneficial to you. You will often have an opportunity to attend actual board meetings and functions with board members. You may have an opportunity to work with board members on various projects. After 1 or 2 years serving in this type of role, you will have access to the board and relationships that can serve you well. Chapter 1, "Board Basics," talks more in depth about advisory boards.

THE CORPORATE GOVERNANCE PATH

Much of the process of landing a spot on a for-profit, or corporate, board will be similar to the process of moving onto nonprofit and advisory boards. The key difference is that corporate boards have a more formalized process for identifying and recruiting new board members.

SEARCH FIRMS

Corporate boards usually use the services of a professional search firm to identify potential board members. They will provide the search firm with the talent matrix that they have developed. They may indicate that they are looking for a new board member and prefer a woman with healthcare and governance experience. This is where your nonprofit or start-up board experience can be valuable. See Chapter 3, "What Nurses Need to Know to Get on Boards(s)," for more on nonprofit or start-up boards.

The top search firms perform the majority of corporate placements in the United States.

There is no cost to do this, and it often results in being contacted by a search consultant who wants to learn more about your specific interests and availability.

After you identify the search firms in your community, send your one-sheet bio, a full resume, and a letter of introduction asking to be placed into the firm's database.

EDUCATION AND INFORMATION

The National Association of Corporate Directors (NACD at www. nacdonline.org) offers many workshops around the country on different aspects of board governance. These workshops are wonderful opportunities to take one of those courses not only for the content of the program, but also for the connections that you will make with others during the session. Because courses are almost always followed up with some kind of social event (a chance to network), select a session close to where you live. You may meet people who are on, or are recruiting for, corporate boards in your area. You may also want to get on their mailing list so you can receive information on issues that affect corporate directors.

Business schools are another source of information; many offer 2- to 3-day programs on corporate governance. So, the important takeaway here is that going to an executive education program at a good business school in your community can be worthwhile, not only in terms of the content provided, but also in terms of the new networking opportunities and visibility that come with the experience.

For instance, I attended a 3-day course offered by Harvard Business School. Prior to the program, I received a packet of 30 corporate case studies with instructions to read and be prepared to discuss my responses to the questions during the session. There were about 70 attendees at the program. It was taught in Harvard's traditional case study method with a professor in the front of the room randomly calling on people and asking them to respond to some pretty tough questions. Often, the professor would pit one person's response against another's, which generated some lively debate. In those three intensive days, I learned a great deal. But, I also learned something else that was interesting. There were several organizations represented in the room that were actually seeking board members. They were observing the attendees to determine who had done their homework; how they responded to the questions directed to them; whether they could tolerate people who had different opinions; and whether they could deal with the ambiguity of the case studies where in some cases, management had been correct but in others, the board was correct. Some attendees were clearly so biased that they could only see one point of view.

After this program, I was contacted by two separate boards and one search firm. I had not even realized that they were in the program looking for board members. One was a long-term care organization that said that I was perfect for them. That board appreciated that I understood healthcare, could see both sides of an issue as well as that sometimes management is correct and sometimes the board is correct, and that I had great governance experience.

The other organization that approached me had nothing to do with healthcare but was actually a big tire company in the automobile industry. That is an area I knew nothing about, and I quickly told them that. This board said, though, that they liked the fact that I was a woman, that I could work with both sides (management and the board), that I compromise when there are different points of view, and that I came with a good governance background. They said, "You could easily learn the automotive industry."

IMPORTANT NEXT STEPS

Looking back on her own career and board experience, Linda Procci says that she wishes she had started sooner. If she had, she says, "It might have changed my professional career." Board experience, she says, opens up an entirely new world of connections. Your fellow board members, she says, "know other people in various industries and they become good resources for you."

Joanne Disch has a similar perspective. In her early board experiences, she says, she had a tendency to underestimate herself and the skills and knowledge she could bring. "That first time I thought, 'Oh, this is so rarified; this is way beyond me—I can't do that,'" she recalls. When she was approached to run for president-elect, she says, "I really anguished, but I decided I would do it and I'm so glad I did." Her advice for other nurses: Avoid the tendency to believe you're not ready. "If you've got good experience, why not give it a shot?"

Laurie Benson, CEO and entrepreneur, urges nurses to look beyond their comfort zones to consider opportunities that might not have ever been on their personal radar. "Bump out your boundaries," she urges. "Get out of your comfort zone. This is where the magic happens. This is where the boardroom appears.

"I don't think anything I've done in the last 30 years has been in my comfort zone. Everything I'm doing is out of my comfort zone. I bump out my boundaries continuously." Doing that, she says, "is exciting, it's emerging, and it keeps me relevant as I learn new things I can contribute in new ways."

Success, says Benson, "doesn't happen in neutral. Always be moving forward, toward your goals."

For nurses, there has never been a better time to leverage the many opportunities available to achieve personal and professional goals. Yes, there will be bumps along the way. Career disappointments are part of the journey, and you should expect them—but, most importantly, learn from them.

"If I was talking to a young nurse, I would say, 'Get in the arena!'" says Gladys Campbell, CNE and clinical strategist. "Don't be afraid to make mistakes. If you wait until you feel you're fully baked to get involved as a leader, you're never going to do it. The longer you wait, the more it will reinforce to you that you don't have the knowledge, skill, ability, or courage.

"None of us ever have it all. I think it's really important for young nurses to not create a habit, or a lifetime, of being a bystander," Campbell says. "We need courageous leaders, not bystanders."

Always keep this thought in mind: When you are through changing, you are through!

As you move forward, commit to spending more time exploiting your strengths and less time bemoaning your weaknesses. The fact that you are reading this book signals that you are considering the possibility of board service in your future. Take the next step today.

6

SERVING AS A PRODUCTIVE BOARD MEMBER

The skills and competencies that you bring to a board role will vary based on your own personal background and experience, the type of board you will be serving, and the qualities and competencies of other board members.

"It's very important to understand what skills and perspectives are represented on the board, and what strategic gaps you are expected to fill when invited to serve," says Laurie Benson, CEO and entrepreneur. "What are those gaps that it's been determined that you could fill?"

How to find out? Ask!

Benson recalls that when asked to serve on her first corporate board since she sold her business, she asked the CEO, "Why, specifically, are you asking me to serve on your board?" His response: "In 20 years of inviting people to serve, no one has ever asked why they were selected."

Make sure to gain clarity as to why you are being asked to serve and what key competencies you can bring forward.

Here is a look at some of the key skills required to serve effectively as a productive member of a board.

STRONG COMMUNICATION SKILLS

Strong communication skills are a must-have for anyone considering a board role. But many nurses are challenged here, says Gladys Campbell, CNE and clinical strategist. "I think nurses often struggle to communicate effectively with non-nurses when we are in our professional roles. It is often a huge barrier for us. Over and over, I have seen nurses who get that seat at the table; and then while sitting on the board, they do not speak. A nurse who does not contribute while in a board role may become through that silence the 'token nurse' or sometimes the 'token woman' if that nurse is female." After nurses get into a board role, says Campbell, they must perform, and good communications are the most significant part of successful board performance.

Effective communication is not just about speaking, of course. Active listening is an important skill for board members, notes Benson. "I don't go into the boardroom with a preconceived idea of what I'm going to recommend," she says. "I listen to the range of options. One of the most important skills I have learned is to be flexible to the right path forward based on the collective intelligence of the group."

In addition to the ability to communicate with others during meetings, board members must be comfortable representing the organization in other settings. "You need to be articulate and know how to speak about your organization," says Susan Hassmiller, executive and senior nurse advisor for the Robert Wood Johnson Foundation.

Here, again, nurses have an edge, says Linda Procci, former COO and VP. Every nurse is trained in the use of Situation, Background, Assessment, and Recommendation (SBAR), a standardized way of communicating that becomes second nature to nurses—identifying the situation, understanding the background, conducting an assessment, and making a recommendation. That same well-recognized process can apply to board work.

"We were taught to think, review the situation, gather the material, and then articulate in a clear and concise way. That's the exact same way you speak in a boardroom," says Procci. Nurses who find themselves intimidated by speaking in a boardroom setting need only reflect on the SBAR to ensure competence and confidence.

Campbell agrees. "We have incredible people skills because we've been dealing with difficult people every single day in the clinical arena," she says.

Boards will inevitably experience conflict, and this is where communication skills are particularly important. Board members, says Pesut, "need skill and talent in understanding competing values and polarities and in terms of not getting caught and bogged down in conflicts or problems that you can't solve, but really it's more about polarities that need to be managed in light of what the mission of the organization is." The ability to engage people in conversations "to unearth and unpack different perspectives and positions in light of greater purposes" is critical, he says.

The politics of governance involve the ability to pull together people from a broad range of backgrounds and perspectives to reach consensus and move the organization forward. Those individuals may be on the board, within the organization, or outside the organization.

"You really have to understand the needs of these other individuals," says Therese Fitzpatrick, clinical strategist and experienced board member. "How do you align everyone's needs and everyone's incentives around solving a problem and continuing to keep the organization profitable?"

HEALTHCARE TRENDS

Politics in healthcare today go beyond the interpersonal, as Fitzpatrick points out. Nurses serving on healthcare boards, in particular, need to "understand how this healthcare organization and system fit into the larger political scene within the state or community."

In today's evolving and increasingly complex healthcare environment, says Fitzpatrick, "Nurses need to have the ability to rethink what it means to be a hospital." They're well positioned to do that, she notes. "That's a real skill set that nurses can bring to the board by virtue of who we are and how we've been socialized in healthcare," she says. "We understand wellness really well. As a matter of fact, we understand it better than many other disciplines within the organization."

COURAGE AND INITIATIVE

Nurses are in a unique position to use their strong backgrounds to help foster change in an increasingly complex system. It takes courage and initiative, but nurses have the experiences and wisdom to navigate the complexity successfully, says Campbell.

"We have an unbelievable understanding of complexity because we work with the most complex system that exists in the world; and literally, we are the last link of a safety chain that stands between a patient and a potentially broken healthcare system or process," Campbell says. "We stand in that gap every single day. We have learned how to be very creative in designing end-arounds to ensure that systems work. We also understand complexity because we are the only clinicians that take care of multiple patients simultaneously. All other clinicians care for patients sequentially. A model of simultaneous care provision creates a level of complexity compression that is significant."

However, because nurses so often spend the majority of their time interacting with each other, "They often don't understand, or recognize, just how unique and valuable these skills are," Campbell says. For a nurse, this is just a normal workday.

Nurses typically understand complexity in healthcare-based organizations better than other clinicians because they manage multiple patients simultaneously, whereas other clinicians manage multiple patients sequentially.

"You've got to have courage," says Campbell. "I've often said that what our hospitals boards need more than anything else right now is flat-out courage. We currently have some healthcare leaders who don't have the necessary knowledge, skill, ability, or courage to transition our care systems to be what is needed: safe, effective, efficient, and patient-centered care.

"Once you're in your mid-50s, you've got 30 years of experience under your belt. You've been through a lot. You've got wisdom; and if you've got wisdom, why wouldn't you have courage?"

"It is constantly an effort of bringing in evidence, bringing in work, bringing in trust," says Hassmiller. And, of course, it involves recognizing the real strengths that you have to bring to bear in a board role. You likely have far more to offer than you realize!

HEALTHCARE TRENDS

Campbell is speaking about the type of courage that allows for tough decision-making and even tougher actions. "A new type of leadership is needed to transform our healthcare system, and it will take courage to move ineffective healthcare leaders out of their positions and to bring in leaders with new ways of thinking and a different set of skills and competencies than what was needed in the past," she says. "These transitions will not be easy."

Finally, advises Benson, "Don't have a personal agenda. Don't join a board for you. Join a board where you can have an impact and bring your competencies in a way that that will have a significant impact."

BEHAVIORAL COMPETENCIES

Board service involves working with and through others, so of course, behavioral competencies are critical. The Blue Ribbon Panel research identified 14 personal behavioral-based capabilities that board members should possess (American Hospital Association's Center for Healthcare Governance, 2009).

The first is **accountability**, which includes creating a culture of accountability throughout the organization and holding the board and leadership accountable for demanding high performance.

The second competency is **achievement orientation**, which focuses on setting high standards, making decisions, and setting goals and priorities based on quantitative measures and performance.

Change leadership (#3) involves maintaining an eye on strategic goals and values during the change process, exhibiting constancy of purpose and consistent leadership throughout periods of change, and envisioning future changes.

Collaboration (#4) involves promoting good working relationships and creating conditions for high-performance teams.

Trustees that act in ways that are **community oriented (#5)** understand the health needs of stakeholders and advocate for them at local, state, and national levels.

Information seeking (#6) is a critical governance capability and involves asking questions, seeking expert perspectives, and ensuring that systems are in place to gather, analyze, and provide information that boards need to set policy and engage in effective decision-making.

Innovation (#7) is becoming part of the infrastructure of today's leading organizations. Innovative thinkers are able to make complex ideas simple to understand, foster new concepts, look at situations in new ways, motivate breakthrough thinking and applications, and deliver products and services in new ways and new models, even with yet-to-be-discovered tools.

Complexity management (#8) is the capability to balance trade-offs, competing interests, and contradictions. Those adept at managing complexity use their highly developed conceptual capacity to understand and deal with a variety of complex issues as well as their implications for the organization's mission, structure, culture, and stakeholders.

To govern effectively for stakeholders, trustees must be **aware of the organization's internal factors (#9)** that drive or block stakeholder satisfaction and organizational performance. This awareness, as well as deeper insight into the actions of stakeholders, the hospital, and the industry can then be put to use to develop support for a national health-care system that promotes long-term population health and wellness.

Trustees also must exhibit **professionalism (#10)** in discharging their duties: that is, embracing improvement in population and individual health and ensuring that the organization values and exhibits professional, patient-oriented and community-oriented behaviors.

Trustees also should play a key role in **building and maintaining relationships (#11)** with influential people in and outside the healthcare field.

Trustees should display a **strategic orientation (#12)** by understanding the forces shaping healthcare and aligning the organization's mission, strategy, and resources to address them.

Board members also must hold management accountable for **developing the organization's talent (#13)** and ensure succession plans are in place for all key leadership positions, including the CEO. Chapter 3, "What Nurses Need to Know to Get on Board(s)," explains those processes.

Finally, board members should model **team-oriented behaviors (#14)** by supporting board goals, reducing obstacles to effectiveness, and coaching and mentoring board members to achieve high performance.

This list of competencies can serve as a starting point for those seeking new board members. It can also provide those interested in board experience with an opportunity to evaluate their own current skill sets to identify areas of opportunity for improvement. Table 6.1 is an example of the type of tool that a board might use when screening and evaluating potential new board members.

TABLE 6.1: SELF-EVALUATION FORM

	My Ranking (1–5)*	Evidence/ Examples to Support	Ideas for Further Development
Accountability			
Achievement orientation			
Change leadership			
Collaboration			
Community orientation			
Information seeking			
Innovation			
Complexity management			
Awareness of organization			
Professionalism			
Relationship building and maintenance			
Strategy orientation			
Talent development			
Team-oriented			
Other (add to the list)			

*1 = novice; 5 = expert

Sound like a big job? It is—but it's highly rewarding as well. If you're up to the challenge, your next step is planning your path to board service. "Nurses often do not have the business acumen that others bring to the table, simply due to lack of experience," says Susan Groenwald, oncology nursing pioneer. "They may also lack knowledge about governance." But, she adds, "All of these knowledge gaps are easily remedied with experience and learning."

REFERENCES

American Hospital Association's Center for Healthcare Governance. (2009). *Competency-based governance: A foundation for board and organizational effectiveness.* http://www.americangovernance.com/resources/reports/brp/2009/

7

WHAT'S HOLDING YOU BACK?

The number of nurses on boards, even healthcare boards, remains woefully low. This metric needs to be changed, and numerous groups—from the Institute of Medicine (2010), to the Robert Wood Johnson Foundation (2014), and many other nursing organizations—are calling for greater representation of women—and especially nurses—in board roles.

Why are few nurses involved in governance? Certainly not due to lack of skill. It can be a challenge to get others to recognize that potential value, however.

One of the issues, says Joanne Disch, former academic executive, professor, and seasoned board member of numerous healthcare organizations, is the "long-held belief across the country that is so pervasive: that if you have a physician on the board, they can speak on any issue." She relays an analogy that she has heard is a twist on the old apples-to-oranges comparison. Nurses, she says, aren't a slice of the apple, with the physicians being the apple. Nurses are the orange and are not subsumed by the physician's expertise. In fact, "what nurses have to offer is complementary and very distinctive."

What are some of the potential drawbacks that keep nurses from being more broadly represented?

REFOCUS EFFORTS

Areas of opportunity for nurses can benefit them and the organizations they serve. Assess your own competencies and take steps to close any gaps you find:

- A general understanding of business principles
- The ability to understand a balance sheet and a profit and loss (P&L) statement
- Recognizing that profit is "a good thing" and why, even for non-profit organizations
- Community and industry experience
- The ability to integrate the knowledge, skills, and experience that you have in a language that all those in the boardroom will understand
- The ability to distill this wisdom down into a few pragmatic points
- Regulatory and compliance knowledge and experience
- Confidence

"Most importantly," says CEO and board consultant Laurie Benson, "nurses need to take a stand after they land a board role. Nobody should wonder where you are coming from in the boardroom. Take a stand when it counts."

There are common areas where nurse leaders may find themselves struggling before they gain board experience.

TOO FOCUSED ON OPERATIONS

One of the things that may hold nurses back, as noted throughout the book, is that their focus is placed too much on nursing and at an operational level, and not enough on the higher-level, strategic issues.

Benson says that her least-rewarding board experiences have been in situations where "there's micro-managing, with too many people wanting to take control." In some cases, she says, boards will recruit seated or former CEOs, "but some CEOs don't know how to act as a board member— they know how to be a great CEO."

Boards are strategic, not operational.

Board members must understand that the board is not operational. Gladys Campbell said she learned this lesson through her various roles in board service. "The learning curve has always been steep and rapid," she says. The experience, though, "has dragged me toward big-picture strategic thinking and progressive learning and confidence building in my board roles. The experience has allowed me to gain clarity on what boards could offer me and what I could offer them."

TOO FOCUSED ON THEIR SHORTCOMINGS

Too often, says executive and nursing advisor Susan Hassmiller, there is a tendency for nurses to be overly focused on their limitations. "Unfortunately," she says, "most of the time, we're focusing on our limitations rather than the capabilities that we bring."

Her advice: "We need to focus more on what we can do and be courageous!"

TOO FOCUSED ON PROBLEM IDENTIFICATION

Nurses, says professor and experienced board member Daniel Pesut, tend to have a problem-solving mindset that focuses on the assessment and identification of problems, rather than an outcome-specification mindset. Both are necessary, he says. "You need to be able to identify the problem, but you also need to figure out where it is you're going and what the system dynamics are around all of the elements and variables associated with the complexities of working on the board. That is still a challenge for [nurses]."

What he has observed is that nurses have a tendency to think of an outcome as the "negative definition of the problem state." For example, if a patient is in pain, and you ask the nurse what the desired outcome is, the nurse would say, "No pain." If the patient were anxious, the nurse would say, "No anxiety." Instead, Pesut says, the outcome for pain might be comfort. The outcome for anxiety might be anxiety controls.

A problem-solving mindset is great for defining the problem space. Pesut believes this skill has been inculcated in nurses through the tradition of the nursing process. He has been an advocate of helping people develop clinical reasoning skills that focus on both problem identification and outcome specification.

Board members need problem-solving skills and outcome specification skills—the ability to contrast a present state with a desired future state.

TOO FOCUSED ON THEIR WORLD VIEW

Gladys Campbell, executive and strategist for nursing organizations, believes the biggest issue holding nurses back from board involvement is their sameness. "I think there is really a clear metaphoric analogy between people of color who are actually multicultural as they shift from their ethnic culture to workplaces that are dominated by a white western European culture, and nursing. As nurses, we tend to be culturally comfortable and competent when talking to ourselves, when we are with 'our people,' 'our club.' But when we move out of our nursing circle, we may experience discomfort within a board culture that is different and unfamiliar. When faced with this situation, a very competent nurse leader may suddenly lack the confidence to speak up or voice dissenting views or opinions. We may feel we don't know what the rules of engagement are in this group. Nurses often say, 'We want a seat at the table,' not realizing that the real challenge is to know what to do with that seat when the table sits within an unfamiliar culture. Like many leaders of color, we need to learn to be multicultural if we are going to succeed as leaders within the dominant culture of the day."

Initially, she says, when sitting in non-nursing board meetings, "I was often unsure of the group norms and concerned about being viewed as only a nursing advocate rather than as a healthcare leader. I was overly conscious of what impression I would make and how I would be perceived or potentially labeled. Early in my board career, I was cautioned that 'no one likes a shrill woman.' As sexist as this comment was, I obviously have not forgotten it. The flip side of all this caution is to also understand and be confident about the unique skills and competencies that nurses bring to the boardroom."

BRING COMPETENCIES TO BEAR

Laurie Benson points to a number of competencies that nurses, in general, can bring to the boardroom:

- **A holistic view:** The ability to recognize the implications of decisions on others.

- **Compatability:** The ability to work in teams across varying disciplines.

- **Accountability:** The ability to set goals that take into account the highest hopes of all stakeholders.

- **Ethics and integrity:** "Nursing is the most trusted profession," reminds Benson. "Bring that trust with you."

- **Operations experience:** An understanding of the complexities of implementing decisions.

- **An understanding of risk management:** "Giving full consideration to risks associated with board decisions."

- **The ability to proactively anticipate and make decisions** with full consideration of risk management and contingencies.

- **Strong communication skills,** including listening skills at a strategic level. This includes hearing what *is* being said as well as what *is not* being said.

- **The ability to take bold action** when necessary.

- **A focus on outcome-based decision-making and servant leadership.** *Servant leadership* means leaders putting themselves or their needs behind the needs of others.

- **The nursing care plan:** "Bring it with you. It works in business too," says Benson.

Susan Groenwald adds, "The most helpful competency is to be someone who can get things done and someone who can work with and through others in a positive manner." Board members must be exceptional communicators, she notes. "The board members that no one wants to work with are those who cannot collaborate, don't listen, aren't open to the views of others, and do not contribute in a positive way," she says.

She adds that, in recruiting board members for Chamberlain's board of trustees, "It was important to have people who believe in and support the mission of the college, who have diverse experience and perspectives, who communicate well with others, and who are collaborative, forward-thinking, and open."

Those who have held the skills required to fill board positions have gained immensely from their experiences. All have had positive experiences—and although some have had less positive experiences, these nurses without exception say that every experience has represented an opportunity to learn and grow.

POSITIVE EXPERIENCES

By and large, nurses feel that their board experiences, despite challenges and struggles along the way, have been positive.

"All of my board experiences have been positive in terms of growth and learning," says Groenwald. "ONS was a start-up, so I learned about by-laws, and I learned the value of Robert's Rules in managing a meeting and achieving the board's goals, hiring, and management of association executives."

Achieve via experience. As president of International Reciprocal Trade Association (IRTA) for a number of years, Groenwald says, she gained additional valuable experience, ultimately leading the association to pass a bill in Congress on behalf of the industry. She led the association to revise its by-laws, hired and managed an association management firm that professionalized the association, and grew membership significantly. During her term as president, the organization also expanded globally. Such significant accomplishments can be both personally and professionally rewarding.

Work together. "When you've got a group of people who are really committed, who are really up-to-date, who listen to each other, and who are really working toward a common goal, it's an incredible experience," says Disch. "I think every board I've been on has had some of that. When you have wonderful staff and wonderful board members, you're just kind of feeding off each other. It's fabulous. When you don't have that, then it's just really not fun."

Practice patience. "Toward the end of my term, the Honor Society was thinking about sun-setting one of its subsidiaries." Pesut was a minority voice in that he wanted to give the new business the chance to develop over time. "Whenever you have a new operation, especially one that has a profit orientation, you've really got to be patient and figure out what works," he says. Pesut prevailed and says he is "glad that they kept the subsidiary alive. I think it's more sustainable now, but at one point in time, there were some pretty tough decisions that had to be made in regards to its viability and its financial success."

Pesut's most positive board experience, he says, was while serving with STTI as president. He particularly recalls the diversity of thought and the way the organization was managed and led at the time. "Nancy Dickenson-Hazard was the CEO when I was president-elect and president, and she really did create an *esprit de corps* among the board members and operations of the organization," he says. "I call these my 'golden years' in terms of governance experience, although there were some challenging decisions that had to be made."

Board service, even when positive, does include challenges. Strong board members will step up to those challenges and embrace the ability to interact with other strong-minded peers in a collegial and collaborative way.

These are the kind of success stories that can evolve even from challenging board experiences. The end result can be rewarding for those who stay the course. Some situations don't result in such positive outcomes, unfortunately. Yet still, the lessons learned are important ones.

Some board decisions can threaten long-standing policies, practices, programs, or people. Keeping eyes on the prize (goals) can help when going through those rough waters.

NEGATIVE EXPERIENCES

Board experiences aren't always positive, of course. But, even when they're not, there are important and valuable lessons to be learned.

While Pesut recalls fondly his work with STTI, another experience wasn't quite so positive. "This was an institution that was originally funded by a philanthropist," he recalls. This founder continued to be involved on the board and, says Pesut, had what he calls "founder's syndrome."

"He operated the board as a monarch and had somewhat of a sovereign archetype to him in terms of dictating how things should be done," says Pesut. This often resulted in a double bind, says Pesut, "where he wanted input from people, but then just by fiat directed how things would be, and that was really pretty challenging." The CEO of the organization, he says, was not very effective, and the combination of these two things led to a "difficult decision-making and dialogue among board members," says Pesut. "It was a difficult time."

Over time, though, the situation turned around. The founder became interested in other things and left, and the CEO also left. "So this was another instance of an organization at a crossroads—a pivot point in terms of whether or not it would survive," says Pesut. He agreed to take the helm and serve as chairman of the board for a year to stabilize the organization and get new leadership on board. And it did turn around. "We had a new president. We had great staff. There were some interesting programs that evolved and developed. And we got some new board members with different perspectives and skill sets. So it went on to develop some major grant funding, and is now actually doing some great work."

Puppet boards exist when a CEO rules or tries to rule indisputably and dictates all board activities and actions. Puppet boards create a dangerous dynamic as board members will still be held accountable for the actions and performance of the organization. Carefully consider your position should you find yourself a part of a puppet board.

Campbell, too, learned an important lesson the hard way during one of her early board experiences. A board had recruited her for a start-up firm that was developing a product to enhance remote physician practice in the area of critical care.

"I was curious," says Campbell, "so I went to look at what they had developed." She saw potential for the product far beyond what the physician leaders of this start-up envisioned. "I watched them run a code remotely. I watched them do a family conference remotely. For me, I thought, 'This isn't about the physicians. This isn't about ICUs. This is about the future of how we handle the healthcare workforce. So I went on the board.'"

Before you sign a contract to be a board member, read the fine print or have an attorney review it. Safe is always better than sorry.

But what she did not do—and that she later regretted—was thoroughly read the contract she signed when she joined the board. "I was, as nurses so often are, so invested in improving this product that I wasn't even thinking about giving away my own intellectual property."

As Campbell's time with the board went on, she came to realize that her vision and the doctors' vision did not converge. "I saw the product's potential as so much broader than the way it was being positioned. As I began raising the issue of having a wider view, I realized the company's founders were not aligned with my thinking. This ultimately resulted in my leaving the board without any compensation for my work or without stock options on the product."

Still, says Campbell, despite this and other tough experiences she has had over the years, she would not go back to change a thing. "I don't think I'd do anything differently because when I think of every mistake I have made, I know I learned valuable lessons from all of them. Some people think you shouldn't take on leadership roles or new experiences until you are thoroughly prepared. I am more of a method actor. I tend to jump in when opportunity presents itself and trust that even when I make mistakes, the learning opportunity will be worth those mistakes."

Board experiences can be less than stellar, too, when the team simply does not work together effectively, says Disch. "No board has been all good or bad, but when you're working with a board member whose goal is really to advance their own agenda, that does not help. I think we've all seen that."

There are situations, she says, where a board member has a singular focus: "where every time they open their mouth, it is 'I'm going to advance diversity,' or 'I'm going to advance rural health.' They're not looking at the issues; they're trying to arbitrate their agenda. That does not help."

Importantly, notes Benson, nurses have the ability to remove themselves from experiences that are not meeting their needs or aligning with their personal values. "I don't stay in negative situations very long," she says. "I either create conditions to move through the negative, or I remove myself." But, she adds: "I'm happy to say I haven't had very many negative experiences." She says she has been fortunate to serve organizations where there is strong leadership, strong corporate cultures and values, and high standards and expectations.

Finally, don't be afraid to take chances or stretch yourself to fill roles that you might not immediately feel confident about. Groenwald recalls one regret as she reflects back on her board experience: "I was offered the opportunity to run for president of ONS, and I turned it down. I might not have been elected, but the experience of running such a top-notch and growing organization like ONS would have been a great experience."

All these experiences, positive and not-so-positive, build competencies.

REFERENCES

Institute of Medicine. (2010). The future of nursing. Author. http://www.thefutureofnursing.org/recommendation/detail/recommendation-7

Robert Wood Johnson Foundation. (December 17, 2014). A goal and a challenge: Putting 10,000 nurses on governing boards by 2020. Author. http://www.rwjf.org/en/library/articles-and-news/2014/12/a-goal-and-a-challenge--putting-10-000-nurses-on-governing-board.html

INDEX

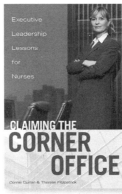
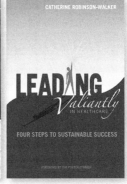